INSTRUCTOR'S GUIDE FOR

SEXUAL INTERACTIONS

Allgeier/Allgeier

Elizabeth Rice Allgeier
Bowling Green State University

Lee Markowitz
Burke Marketing Services, Inc.

Albert Richard Allgeier
Wood County Mental Health Clinic

D.C. HEATH AND COMPANY • Lexington, Massachusetts   Toronto

Published simultaneously in Canada.

Printed in the United States of America.

International Standard Book Number: 0-669-05239-6

TABLE OF CONTENTS

INTRODUCTION

The organization of our Instructor's Guide is based on our experience with using the manuals provided for other texts. Most
of those manuals are organized so that the chapters correspond
with text chapters. Instead, we have organized this manual by
function. Part 1 contains film descriptions, part 2 provides
suggestions for the use of class time, and part 3 contains
evaluation items.

Part 1 of this manual provides a comprehensive review of the
audiovisual materials produced during the past ten years that
are available to supplement each chapter. This section should
be consulted prior to the course to increase your chances of
obtaining desired films on appropriate dates. In addition,
you may want to send a form letter requesting copies of the
latest catalog to each of the film distributors. We've listed
their addresses for your convenience.

Part 2 provides an outline of each chapter with suggestions
for lecture and classroom exercises. With the exception of
the material on anatomy and physiology which tends to be difficult for many students to master, our own lectures do not
duplicate the material covered in the text. Thus, part 2 contains additional material for lectures, class demonstrations,
and exercises.

Part 3 contains test questions for evaluation, with page
numbers on which the answers to the items may be found as that
saves a great deal of time in dealing with student-instructor
disagreements.

The preparation of this manual involved the writing of evaluation items by Lee Markowitz, the preparation of film reviews
by Elizabeth Allgeier and Randolf Sokol, and the suggestions
for lecture material by both Allgeiers.

Finally, we have found this course a great pleasure, and we
hope that you enjoy the opportunity to teach it as much as we
have. We welcome for the next edition suggestions, reports of
your own research and/or teaching strategies that you've found
successful.

PART I: REVIEW OF AUDIO-VISUAL MATERIALS

At the time that books are ordered for the coming term, it is
a good idea to order films for the course. The following list
of films is organized sequentially by chapter. Most manuals
list relatively few films, but we have chosen to review a large
number of films that have been produced since 1974. Movies
predating 1974 are included only if we think that they are
especially good, or if there is nothing more current on the
topic.

We have shown many of these films in our classes and have obtained student ratings on a number of them using 7-point scales,
with 7 indicating that the student strongly recommends that the
film be ordered for subsequent semesters, and 1 indicating
strong recommendation that it not be ordered. For other
films, we have abstracted catalog descriptions. If you show
a film and obtain student ratings that you are willing to
share with us for future editions of the Instructor's Guide,
we would appreciate the information.

Prices are based on 1982 or 1983 catalog listings and are
shown in the order of purchase/rental. In some cases, we
have also listed the less expensive rental rates provided
by Pennsylvania State University (PSU) for a particular
film. In addition, you may be able to obtain similar dis-
count rates from other universities in your part of the
country if they own the film.

The names and addresses of film distributors are listed at
the end of Part 1 for your convenience. To save space, we
are using the following codes in the film reviews:
    CD: Catalog Description (our abstract).
    AD: Allgeiers' Description.
    SR: Student Rating. These are all based on the mean
        ratings of human sexuality students at Bowling Green
        State University in 1983 (7 = should definitely re-
        order, 1 = should definitely not reorder).

INTRODUCTION

A quickie (1970). Multi Media, #I 56, 1 min, 48 sec., B & W,
music only, $55/$14. AD: Amusing speeded-up version of a
sexual encounter that can be used to desensitize students'
initial anxieties about the course content. Could also be
used with Ch. 8 prior to more explicit sexual interaction
films.

<u>Mammalian Sexual Behavior</u>. Kinsey Institute, B & W, silent
with subtitles. Available for the cost of copying (about $45
per reel, 2 reels). AD: Amusing, grainy-quality film showing
the sexual behavior of a number of mammals from cats through
elephants with their prehensile penises. We ask students to
note similarities and differences with human copulation, and
also ask them to define "sex" after seeing the film. Good for
desensitizing students through laughter.

<u>Orange</u> (1970). Multi Media, #I 52, 2 min, 40 sec., color,
$68/$14. AD: This is a beautifully filmed and erotic movie
of an orange being opened. Provides a good basis for discussing sensuality and arousal.

CHAPTER 1: PERCEPTIONS OF SEXUALITY:
HISTORICAL AND CROSS-CULTURAL OVERVIEW

<u>A Cross-Cultural Approach to the Acquisition of Sex Roles and
Social Standards</u> (1975). 23 min., color, $360/$36, PSU rental:
$16.50 CD: Discusses the acquisition of sexual standards and
sex roles. Learning is demonstrated by observation, imitation,
praise, and punishment. Guatemala, Kenya, and Japan are used
to illustrate similarities and differences.

<u>Kypseli: Women and Men Apart: A Divided Reality</u> (1976).
37 min., color, PSU: $540/$23.50. CD: Peasants of Kypseli,
an isolated village on a Greek island are shown dividing time,
space, material possessions, and activities according to an
underlying pattern based on the separation of males and females.
This division, in turn, determines the village social structure.

CHAPTER 2: CONTEMPORARY EXPLANATIONS OF HUMAN SEXUALITY

<u>Thank You Mask Man</u>. Grove, 9 min., color, $200/$25. This is
an animated version of a Lenny Bruce routine that deals with
sexual attitudes, obscenity and myth-making. This can be
used as an introduction to the theories chapter in that Bruce,
in a sense, was questioning the theories about the relationship of sex to filth and sin held by many members of our
society. We attempt, in the introduction to that chapter, to
point out that we all hold implicit theories about sexuality,
and Bruce was perhaps more aware of our common assumptions
than most people in his time.

<u>Sociobiology: Doing What Comes Naturally</u> (1974). 22 min.,
color, PSU rental: $15.50. CD: Irven DeVore discusses the
possibility of universal laws that govern behavior. Compares
baboon aggression and sex to the behavior of humans and what
this means for the future of our species.

Sociobiology: The Human Animal (1977). 54 min., color. PSU
rental: $27.50. CD: Documentary on sociobiology, in which
proponents argue that without consideration of biology, the
study of human culture makes no sense. Opponents denounce
the theory as reactionary political doctrine with no scientific basis which could be used to probe the supremacy of races
or male dominance and therefore justify social inequality.
Edward Wilson and Richard Lewontin argue the issues: AD: The
CD suggests that this film provides an example of the misunder-
standing of theory as advocacy that we discuss in the book,
and this might be pointed out to students prior to showing the
film.

CHAPTER 3: RESEARCH ON SEXUALITY

The Sexes: Breaking the Barriers (1975). Document, 18 min.,
color, $275/$40. PSU rental: $15.50. AD: Largely based on
interviews with Masters and Johnson regarding changing sexual
roles, increasing enlightenment, sex education, sexual dysfunction, and homosexuality. This may be useful during discussion of the research methods used by Masters and Johnson.
Our students weren't particularly impressed with this film.

Physiological Responses of the Sexually Stimulated Female in
the Laboratory (1975). Focus, 16 min., color, $320/$50.
AD: Shows internal and external responses to sexual stimulation as originally described by Masters and Johnson, including
explicit footage of genitals during pre-orgasmic, orgasmic,
and resolution stages. This film is more relevant for Ch. 8,
however our students commented that it was rather dry and
clinical, so it may effectively be used in conjunction with
discussion of Masters & Johnson's research methods in Ch. 3.

Physiological Responses of the Sexually Stimulated Male in
the Laboratory (1975). Focus, 16 min., color, $320/$50. See
above description.

Pomeroy Takes a Sex History (1972). Multi Media, 35 min.,
color, $445/$60. AD: The use of the interview to obtain a
sex history is demonstrated by Dr. Wardell Pomeroy, one of
the collaborators in the Kinsey studies who reports collecting over 10,000 histories. This film is perhaps a bit long
for the point it makes, but it does provide a good example
of nonjudgmental interviewing.

CHAPTER 4: SEXUAL ANATOMY AND PHYSIOLOGY

The Miracle of Life (1982). Time-Life, 57 min., color.
We have no price for this outstanding NOVA film, but most of
the Time-Life video cassettes sell for about $200. If your
university has a TV station, they may be able to show it for

your class over closed-circuit. AD: This is the latest effort of the photographer Lars Nilsson, essentially showing the voyage of the sperm and the egg from the testicles and ovary, their union, and subsequent prenatal development. We concur with our students' rating (the highest we've ever seen) that if you can show only one film, this is the one to select: SR: 6.56. Out of 225 students, 4 reported boredom; most of them used adjectives such as "incredible," "amazing," "beautiful," "outstanding," etc.

The Sexually Mature Adult (1973). Media Guild, 16 min., color, $312/$30. AD: Uses diagrams and photography with four different couples to show anatomy and physiology involved with the sexual response cycle. Men and women discuss the ways they respond to various stimuli and share some of their feelings about various points in the cycle. We have used this film primarily in the context of material presented in Ch. 8, but it could also be used when Ch. 4 is covered, as the diagrams are excellent. The film was made prior to the publication of research on the Grafenberg spot and female ejaculation, so instructors may want to comment on that.

Your Pelvic and Breast Examination. Perennial, 12., color $199/$23.50. CD: A young woman examines her breasts for lumps, and this procedure plus the purposes of pelvic exams are shown. Also demonstrates the administration of pap smears and gonorrhea cultures.

To Discover Your Body's Time Clock: Anticipate the Rhythms of Your Ecstacy and Blues (1976). 20 min., color, PSU rental, $15.50. CD: Analysis of biorhythms; correlation of lunar movements with the female menstrual cycle, sexual incompatibility due to out-of-phase metabolic cycle, change in body rhythm in response to stress, relationship between biorhythm in response to stress, relationship between biorhythms variations and behavioral changes.

CHAPTER 5: PRENATAL DEVELOPMENT AND GENDER DIFFERENTIATION

When Life Begins. CRM/McGraw Hill, 101912-X, 14 min., $265/$26. CD: Examines fetal development from conception to birth. Development of the external organs of the fetus is shown, concluding with a live birth.

See also Miracle of Life (Ch. 4).

CHAPTER 6: GENDER IDENTITIES AND GENDER ROLES

Morning After. Filmakers, 17 min., $375/$40. CD: A vignette showing a seemingly composed young man suffering with his vulnerability over the break-up of a long relationship. He plays the "singles game" and fantasy takes over. He wonders if his girlfriend was right about his unresponsiveness. Looks at male gender roles and interpersonal communication.

Apres Le Soiree (1976). Multi Media, 11 min., B & W, $220/$25. CD: Using stereotypic humor, shows an older man and younger woman after a night out returning to her room. She flirts but falls asleep. The man unsuccessfully tries to awaken her. In the morning, she wakes up refreshed and leaves. CD suggests that it is good for discussion on gender roles, dating behavior, and attitudes about sex.

Dressing Up: An Overview of Cross Dressing (1979). Multi Media, 16 min., color, $200/$25. CD: Male cross dressing is portrayed in occupational, experimental, and transvestite contexts.

First Date (1977). Multi Media, 5 min., color, $75/$17. CD: Deals with role models. A young man and woman on their first date reverse traditional gender roles. The woman seduces the man, and the film concludes with a satisfied woman and a dissatisfied man. Satirizes traditional gender roles.

Am I Normal? New Day, 24 min., color, $425/$45. Depicts the experiences that boys go through during puberty. Describes male development and raises issues about masculinity, identity, and peer pressure.

Dear Diary. New Day, 25 min., color, $425/$45. CD: Amusing film about female puberty that raises questions that girls have during adolescence. Discusses female growth and development, and deals with issues of self-image and peer pressure to date. Has won numerous awards.

Who's Doing It? Sexual Attitudes in America (1982). Multi Media, 13 min., $260/$39. CD: Explores the current attitudes in America in an interview format with people across the life-span. Frank discussion of issues related to sexuality. Looks at the problems of maintaining lasting relationships as well as gender roles and the degree to which these roles interfere with relationships.

What Guys Want (1983). Polymorph, 16 min., $395/$40. CD: Teens express their attitudes and feelings about maleness and their sexual behavior.

Sexuality: A Woman's View (1981). Multi Media, 30 min., $510/$75. Explores question of relative enjoyment of women and men of sex. Focuses on traditional stereotypes that have inhibited women's sexuality. Twelve women in a seminar on sexuality exchange their ideas, upbringing, and experiences with sex. Need for cooperation and communication between women and men emphasized. May also be shown in Chs. 8 and 9.

The Sexes: What's the Difference? (1972). Filmaker, 28 min., color, $425/$45. PSU rental: $18.50. CD: Addresses the nature/nurture question regarding gender roles; based on work by J. Kagan and E. Maccoby.

The Sexes: Roles (1972). Filmaker, 28 min., color, $425/$45, PSU rental: $18.50. CD: Surveys the evolution of male-female roles from prehistorical to current times. Includes information from animal studies. Can be used with the above film in sequence (purchase and rental of both: $750/$75).

Self-Identity/Sex Roles. CRM/McGraw Hill, 16 min., color, $195/$20. CD: Three related females with three different lifestyles begin to understand each other.

Women: The Hand That Cradles The Rock. Document, 20 min., color, $300/$40. AD: Presents women holding both feminist and traditional attitudes toward gender roles, marriage and childrearing. Albert Ellis and Phyllis Chesler appear in one of the discussion sequences. This is an excellent film for stimulating discussion of changing gender roles. We ask students to write down their gender and to name the person they most and least admired in the film and the reasons for their evaluations. We then collect the comments, have the students form small (4 or 5 people) same gender groups and redistribute the responses of the other gender to each group with each member reading one, and discussing them. We then combine two groups (one male and one female) and have them discuss the movie and their comments. Generally, each gender is surprised by the similarity of the responses of the other gender to the movie; students get so involved in this exercise that unless your class sessions last longer than 90 minutes, it tends to take the whole class period to show the movie and discuss students' comments. SR: 3.66.

Sex Role Development (1974). CRM/McGraw-Hill, 23 min., color, $295/$35, PSU rental: $15.50. Examines methods of eliminating sexual stereotyping of youngsters.

Sex and Gender (1976). Multi Media, #I 60, 20 min., B & W, $310/$45. CD: Explores attitudes about gender identity through candid interviews with transsexuals and transvestites interspersed with sequences of professional female impersonators backstage. Virginia Prince, Ph.D. (nee Charles Prince) adds comments on transvestite and transsexual phenomena.

Killing Us Softly: Advertising's Image of Women (1980).
Cambridge, 30 min., color, $550/$106 (1 week), $61 (2 days),
$46 (1 day). May be purchased for $450 if use is limited to
one institution. AD: This is a delightful film of Jean
Kilbourne's presentation and the audience's reaction to her
narration in the context of a series of slides of ads that
appear harmless. She is clearly able to deal with the sexism
of these ads in a humorous and nonvindictive manner that is
very effective, and she moves toward the more damaging ads
toward the end that involve violence against women. This is
a superb film that we like so much that we risk the redundancy
of showing it in both our human sexuality and psychology of
gender classes.

What Guys Want (1983). Polymorph, 16 min., color, $395/$40.
CD: Adolescent males from diverse ethnic, racial and economic
backgrounds candidly express their attitudes and feelings
about maleness and their male behavior including "one night
stands," commitment and marriage, virginity and peer pressure,
their first sexual experience, contraception, fear of rejection and fatherhood. Examines values and helps teen of both
genders understand the consequences of sexual behavior.

See also, Cross-Cultural Approach to the Acquisition of Sex
Roles and Social Standards (Ch. 1); The Sexes: Breaking the
Barriers (Ch. 3); Kypseli: Women and Men Apart (Ch. 1);
Radical Sex Styles (Ch. 20); and Valerie (Ch. 20).

CHAPTER 7: SEXUAL AROUSAL, FANTASIES, AND FEELINGS

A Film About Sharon (1976). Multi Media, $I 97, 19 min.,
color, $310/$45. CD: Deals with pornography and is presented
with a mixture of documentary and erotically explicit sexuality.
Sharon is described as an attractive educated, young woman who
has achieved commercial success, recognition, and satisfaction
as a "porn actress." Sharon discusses her background and experiences that play a part in her life as a sexual being both
commercially and personally. Validates the notion that women
enjoy sex.

Sweet Dreams (1979). Multi Media, E# 68, 13 min., color,
$255/$37. CD: Combines erotic fantasy with one woman's
masturbation pattern. Narration from the character, a lesbian,
explains that her sexual preference does not preclude fantasiz-
ing about males. She also discusses the role that masturbation
plays in her life.

Dirty Business (1976). Multi Media, #I 25, 25 min., color,
$360/$55. CD: Includes interviews with people involved with
buying, selling, acting in, and making underground sex films.

Auto-Erotic (1981). Multi Media, #I 93, 7 min., color, $110/ $20. CD: A fantasy film on the love affair many American males have with their automobiles. Discusses the sexual aura surrounding the car in our society. Subject demonstrates his fantasy relationship with his car.

See also Orange (Introduction).

CHAPTER 8: SEXUAL BEHAVIOR

Masturbation: Men (1979). Multi Media, #I 82, 18 min., color, $300/$40. CD: Four men between the ages of 20 and 50 share their patterns of masturbation. The film is set in each of their respective homes and they are shown masturbating. Each man discusses his attitudes toward masturbation, how and when he began, use of fantasy, frequency, and role this activity currently plays in his adult life.

Female Masturbation. Focus, 6 min., color, $125/$25. CD: Provides a direct portrayal of self-pleasuring. Addresses the physiology and psychology of this practice.

Male Masturbation. Focus, same description as above film.

Sun Brushed (1974). Multi Media, 14 min., color, $225/$40. CD: A young heterosexual couple is shown making love on a deck overlooking the beach. After talk and warm looks, they engage in a variety of sexual activities including oral sex, woman above coitus, and mutual pleasuring.

Self Loving (1976). Multi Media, 34 min., color, $440/$60. CD: Cross-cultural exploration of female sexuality, filmed in rural and urban environments with 11 young heterosexual, homosexual, and bisexual young women who describe early experiences, current sexual patterns, and feelings about masturbation and sexual interaction.

Expressions of Love (1981). Multi Media, #I 87, 32 min., color, $440/$60. CD: Shows one couple's sexual pattern while narration discusses their sexuality and the role it plays in their lives. Wide variety of sexual activities is shown including massage, cunnilingus, fellatio, manual stimulation, and various coital positions. Communication between partners is stressed.

Playmates (1977). Multi Media., 12 min., color, $250/$37. CD: Sexual playfulness and communication is emphasized in this film which portrays a couple who are very sensitive to each other's desires. A variety of sexual techniques are shown including breast stimulation, fellatio, cunnilingus, and coitus.

Intimacy (1981). Multi Media, #I 101, 34 min., color, $200/
$30. CD: Explores the role of sex in human relationships and
notes that sex is a part of what we are and not just something
we do. Pyramid theory is presented which has 7 levels: from
hand holding to orgasm. Discusses enjoyment of lower levels
for their own sake at times.

Orgasmic Expulsions of Fluid in the Sexually Stimulated Female
(1981). Focus, 9 min., color, $190/$30. AD: Graphic photo-
graphs of the expulsion of fluid from the urethra in several
women in response to Grafenberg spot stimulation. Shows how
to locate the Grafenberg spot and discusses lab analyses comparing the fluid to urine. Describes the embarrassment and
concern of women in the past to fluid expulsion when they believe they are urinating. Beverly Whipple, one of the primary
researchers in the area, plays the role of the counselor in
the film. SR: 4.98; students found the film "amazing," but
also reported some discomfort over the explicitness of the
genital responses.

Sexual Intercourse. Focus, 17 min., color, $295/$50.
CD: Describes physiological respones and behavior during
intercourse, and discusses emotional factors related to sex
such as intimacy, communication, sharing, attitudes, etc.

Love and the Art of Sexual Fulfillment. Grove, 28 min.,
color, $475/$50. CD: An attractive, young married couple
graphically demonstrate the methods by which they give each
other sexual pleasure. Narrated by a physician who discusses
the contribution made to their mutual gratification by the
couple's affection and respect for each other.

Marsha and Harry (1982). Fcous, 10 min., $225/$30, color.
CD: Humorously examines the difficulties and pleasures of
first time intercourse. Marsha and Harry are personified as
vagina and penis puppets (by Jim Jackson) in whith they discuss their fears and anxieties and confront the awkwardness
of foam and condom contraceptives.

The New Sexuality (1974). 26 min., color, PCR rental: $18.50.
CD: NBC documentary on changing attitudes toward sexuality.
Discusses sex in the media, the women's liberation movement,
and the alienation of youth. People involved in alternative
lifestyles describe their activities and relationships. Behavioral experts discuss sex therapy, surrogate sex, and counseling.

See also, Sexuality: A Woman's View (Ch. 6); The Sexually
Mature Adult (Ch. 4); Massage (Ch. 7); Sweet Dreams (Ch. 7);
A quickie (Ch. 8); Physiological Responses of the Sexually
Stimulated Female in the Laboratory (Ch. 3); and Physiologi-
cal Responses of the Sexually Stimulated Male in the Laboratory
(Ch. 3).

CHAPTER 9:   SEXUAL DYSFUNCTIONS AND THERAPY

Why Didn't You Tell Me? Focus, 11 min., B & W, $200/$30.
CD: A young woman finally overcomes emotional barriers to
tell her partner that she is nonorgasmic. He is initially
shocked, but communication is opened, and the emphasis is on
interaction and open communication between partners.

Sharing Orgasm: Communicating Your Sexual Responses. Focus,
color, 10 min., $260/$30. CD: Shows genital pleasuring as a
crucial first step for women learning to have orgasms with
their partners. Discusses specific exercises, sharing of feelings, techniques, and the importance of communication.

Diagnostic Methods in Male Impotence (1983). Multi Media, 16
min., $320/$50. CD: Demonstrates various diagnostic methods,
and discusses vascular casts, sexual history, vascular states,
penile palpation, genital reflexes, nocturnal penile
tumescence, artificial erection, etc. Does not describe the
many psychological problems that can lead to dysfunction, but
emphasizes diagnostic procedures.

Diagnosing Erectile Problems. Focus, 20 min., color, $385/
$60. CD: Detailed discussion addressing both physiological
and psychological problems. Clinical emphasis and diagnostic
procedures presented.

Treating Erectile Problems. Focus, 20 min., color, $385/$60.
This film can be obtained with the above film for $695/$110.
CD: Presents clinical treatment techniques with a man and
woman present, and considers both physiology and psychology.

Three Styles of Marital Conflict (1978). Research Press, 14
min., color, $255/$50. CD: Depicts three common styles of
marital conflict with true-to-life vignettes of couples.

Becoming Orgasmic: A Sexual Growth Program for Women. Focus,
52 min., color, $320/$50 for each film. CD: This series of
3 films is designed for women who have difficulty having
orgasm with a partner. Through a series of self exploration
exercises developed by Joseph LoPiccolo and W. C. Lobitz,
women discover how to give themselves pleasure and eventually
teach their partners what they have learned. Film 1, Self-
Discovery, shows a woman exploring her genitals and discover-
ing areas of her body that give her pleasure. She describes
her fears and hesitations about what she is doing. Film 2,
Pleasuring, shows the woman experimenting with the use of
erotic literature, fantasy, orgasm triggers, vibrators, and
body movement exercises. Feeings that can interfere with
"letting go" are discussed. Film 3, Sharing, shows the woman
pleasuring herself in the presence of her partner and then

guiding him as he learns to please her effectively. Intercourse
and concurrent manual stimulation with positions to facilitate
it are depicted, and good communication is emphasized.

See also Sexuality: A Woman's View (Ch. 6) and The New
Sexuality (Ch. 8).

CHAPTER 10:   CONCEPTION AND PREGNANCY

Fullness (1974). Multi Media, 13 min., color, music only.
$255/$37. CD: A young couple shares their relationship and
sexuality when she is 8 months pregnant. They flow easily
into sexual activity, and she performs fellatio and he manipu-
lates her genitals. Atmosphere is gentle and caring, depict-
ing some of the possibilities for sexual activity in the latter
stages of pregnancy.

One, Two, Three, Zero: Infertility (1981). Filmaker's, 28
min., color, $425/$45. CD: Follows several couples who have
had trouble conceiving. A variety of problems are described,
and the strain placed on both partners and on the marriage is
discussed. Most couples persevere, and through treatment or
adoption, have a family. American Film Festival, 1981.

Emotional Aspects of Pregnancy (1977). Perennial, #1079,
20 min., color, $332/$39. CD: Designed to prepare expectant
parents for the emotional changes of pregnancy, the film high-
lights the experiences of two expectant couples and one
expectant single woman, and deals with changes in sexuality,
relationships, and dreams.

See also When Life Begins (Ch. 5).

CHAPTER 11:   BIRTH

Five Women, Five Births: A Film About Choices (1978).
Multi Media, 28 min., B & W, $395/$45. CD: Records the
intimacy of childbirth with five women describing their
thoughts about pregnancy and birth. Spontaneous dialogue
during and after the birth. Alternatives to traditional
hospital birth are presented.

Fathers. New Day (1982), 26 min., color, $385/$50. CD:
Warm portrayal of men's relationships with their own children.
A variety of fathers discuss their feelings about pregnancy
and childbirth, showing affection, job and home life, changes
in women's and men's roles, and masculine behavior. Comments
by Dr. H. B. Biller provide a more rounded view of today's
fathers. Award winner.

Birth of a Family. Perennial, $1051, 24 min., color, $360/$42.
AD: Well done presentation of childbirth preparation classes
and the actual labor and delivery process. Shows the reactions
of both parents, and discusses pain, although the woman appears
to experience relatively little pain. The importance of par-
ticipation by the father and childbirth preparation is
emphasized. The strongest student reaction is to the episiotomy
and cutting of the umbilical cord. Students should be told
ahead of time that both are painless, and the movie can be
followed with a discussion of the childbirth controveries
material in the text. SR: 6.52.

Labor of Love: Childbirth Without Violence. Perennial,
#1061, 27 min., color, $387/$46. AD: Narrated by Art Ulene,
this film contrasts the use of the Leboyer method with a traditional delivery. Since one aspect of Leboyer delivery
involves reduced lighting, and actual Leboyer birth is difficult to see. Interviews Art Janov (primal scream therapy)
who connects his work with the importance of gentle birthing.
Presents pro and con statements by physicians regarding this
method of birth.

A Baby is Born (Revised, 1977). Perennial, #1015-17, 23 min.,
color, $360/$42. AD: Depicts couple and doctor through the
process of a long labor and birth. Deals with the purposes
of episiotomy and parental concerns and anxieties. The birth
process is well filmed, but some of our students wondered how
typical the physician's behavior was in accompanying the father
to the locker room to change his clothes, and so forth. Provides a description of a postnatal visit in which the doctor
discusses the spacing of conceptions through using contraceptives.
Our students prefer Birth of a Family (see above).

Birth: Parts 1 and 2 (1977). 57 min., color, PSU: $760/$31.
CD: Critique of childbirth practices in Western society.
Argues against impersonal, routine hospital procedures and
calls for a more humanitarian approach toward the feelings of
mother and child. Commentary by R. D. Laing.

Talking about Breastfeeding. Polymorph, 17 min., color,
$295/$30. CD: The effect of breastfeeding on children and
mothers is discussed through interviews with women. Considers
breastfeeding and C-sections, premature delivery, pressure
from relatives, sibling rivalry, and continuation of careers.

Learning to Breastfeed. Polymorph, 22 min., color, $395/$40.
CD: Describes initial nursing experiences, differences among
babies and mothers at birth, and what can be done if problems
arise. One woman is shown nursing 20 min. after delivery, and
a hospital class on breastfeeding for women who deliver
vaginally or via C-section is filmed. Sore and inverted nipples,
encorgement and the role of oxytocin are discussed as are

returning to work and the importance of the psychological aspects of lactation.

See also When Life Begins (Ch. 5); The First Days of Life (Ch. 5).

CHAPTER 12: CONTRACEPTION

Hope is Not a Method-II. Perennial, #1005, 17 min., color, $276/$33. CD: Provides medical information on withdrawal, rhythm, spermicidal foams, condoms, diaphragms, pills, IUDs, vasectomy, tubal ligation, and abortion.

Condom Sense (1981). Perennial, #1117. 25 min., color, $450/$45. CD: Encourages male contraceptive responsibility through the use of humor and examinations of myths. Has won numerous awards.

Bob's Vasectomy (1977). Multi Media, 12 min., color, $250/ $37. CD: A 47 year old man describes his reasons for having a vasectomy. The surgical procedure is shown and demonstrated to be painless. Includes comments of several men of varied backgrounds who have had vasectomies.

See also Marsha and Harry (Ch. 8).

CHAPTER 13: RESOLVING UNWANTED PREGNANCY

Growing Up Fast, What Every Service Provider Show Know About Teenage Parenthood (1979). Multi Media, #1 94, 31 min., color, $200/$30. CD: Should teenage parents addressing issues such as family involvement, ambivalence about pregnancy, problems between partners as a result of the pregnancy, abortion, etc.

Janet's Abortion (1976). Multi Media, #I 39, 12 min., color, $250/$37. CD: Follows a 23 year old woman through an actual abortion in the 14th week of pregnancy. The abortion is performed in a doctor's office using the laminaria procedure and is very graphic. Discusses how the woman experienced each step of the abortion.

Teenage Pregnancy and Prevention (1982). Human Relations Media, 632-RN, 3 part program, $119. CD: This film series addresses the problem, choices, and solutions. Also discusses the emotional, social, and financial difficulties facing pregnant teens and their partners. Stresses the need for greater responsibility by both males and females.

Girl on the Edge of Town (1983). Media Guild, Paulist Productions, 25 min., color, $445/$35. CD: Discusses teenage pregnancy, abortion, and the responsibility of living with one's decisions. These issues are presented in the context of a family whose teenaged daughter is pregnant.

Boys and Girls Together (1979). Media Guild, 29 min., color, $545/$50, PSU rental: $24. CD: An edited version of an "outstanding" TV documentary. Examines the facts and ramifications of teenage pregnancy, and presents interviews with adolescents, their families, and workers in the field, and suggests possible solutions.

A Far Cry from Yesterday. Perennial, # 1022-68, 20 min., color, $332/$39. AD: Presents a dramatized version of what happens to the early passionate relationship of a teenaged couple who were using foam, but stopped because it was too much trouble. They marry because of pregnancy, and scenes of early optimism are interposed with scenes after the arrival of the baby at which point the parents engage in constant arguments. Our students think that the portrayal of the problems are overdone, but the film is useful for introducing a discussion of marriage motivated by pregnancy.

Four Young Women. Perennial, #1044, 20 min., color, $332/$39. AD: Four women describe their reasons for choosing abortion. Situations include an unmarried couple who are not ready for marriage, a woman who ends a relationship when she discovers that she is pregnant, a couple who married because of pregnancy and are experiencing a second unplanned pregnancy, and an unmarried high school student. The film ends with a short discussion of the medical aspects of abortion, and the importance of contraceptive use. Students have commented that the presentations seem overly optimistic, but the movie is well done.

Young, Single and Pregnant (1973). Perennial, #1043, 18 min., color, $298/$35, PSU rental: $114.50. AD: Similar in format to Four Young Women, except that the four women who are portrayed discuss their reasons for the choices of adoption, abortion, marriage, and single parenthood when they became pregnant. SR: 5.30.

Early Abortion. Perennial, #1055, 8 min., color, $144/$17. AD; Narrated by Adrienne Barbeau, this film provides a clear description of the use of vacuum aspiration abortion through diagrams. The actual procedure is filmed, and there is a group question and answer session dealing with the after effects of abortion, post-abortion infection, effects of abortion on future pregnancy, and the length of time until menstruation returns.

When Teens Get Pregnant. Polymorph, 18 min., color, $395/
$40. CD: Actual females who have become pregnant relate
poignantly their feelings, fears, realities, etc.

CHAPTER 14:   SEXUALITY EARLY IN THE LIFE SPAN

Sexual Development in Children (1983). Multi Media, 45 min.,
$410/$60. CD: Format is a video-taped lecture presentation
in which the speaker discusses and explores the developmental
process of the sexual life of boys and girls from infancy
through puberty. Discusses the prohibitions directed against
the expression of childhood sexuality, and notes that sex is
a potential source of pleasure for people of all ages including children.

Human Sexuality and the Life Cycle (1982). Human Relations
Media, #745-PN, $119 for 3-part slide/tape program. Part 1:
Infancy and Childhood; Part 2: Adolescent Sexuality;
Part 3: Adult Sexuality. CD: Surveys sexuality at all
stages of human development. Compares the attitudes of various cultures toward sexual behavior. Discusses teenage
pregnancy, masturbation, homosexuality, and sexual dysfunction.

Sexuality: The Human Heritage (1975). NET program, 59 min.,
color, PSU: $635/$27. Development of human sexual identity.
Jerome Kagan discusses how children acquire gender and role
identity. Teenagers describe the peer pressure they feel to
have early sexual relations. Homosexuals explain how they
view themselves in relation to the standards of society.
Gender roles in marriage, sex in old age, and menopause are
some of the topics explored.

See also A Cross-Cultural Approach to the Acquisition of Sex
Roles and Social Standards (Ch. 1).

CHAPTER 15:   ADOLESCENCE AND YOUNG ADULTHOOD

Myth Conceptions (A Teenage Sex Quiz) (1980). Multi Media,
18 min., color, $300/$40. CD: Portrays a peer group
education program for jr. and sr. high school age youth.
Explores traditional questions about sex and parenting; what
is commonly believed, and what is actually true. Issues
include birth control, teen parenting, STDs, and the decision
as to whether or not to be sexually active. AD: May be useful for discussion of sex ed.

Achieving Sexual Maturity (1973). Media Guild, 21 min.,
color., $395/$35, PSU rental: $13. AD: Good description
of sexual anatomy and physiology using well-done diagrams

and explicit live footage of nude adults. Moves from conception and embryonic development through childhood, puberty and adolescence showing the parallels between female and male development. Discusses ovulation, menstruation, ejaculation, and nocturnal emission. We've shown this to half a dozen classes and asked them to indicate the portion of the film with which they were least comfortable. The male and female masturbation sequences are explicit and do seem to cause discomfort so they should be discussed following the film. Although our students generally like this film, they also comment on it being "dated," as the actors' dress and hairstyles are reminiscent of the latter 1960s on the west coast. SR: 4.48.

Would You Kiss a Naked Man? Perennial, #1048, 20 min., color, $332/$39. AD: Explores teenage attitudes and behaviors toward sexuality and morality. Focuses on sexual role playing, values clarification, sexual games, the concept of "love," the search for commitment, peer group influences, parent-child relationships, nudity, and virginity. Contains a short, relatively modest nude scene. Our students think that it is below their level of sophistication.

Adolescent Sexual Conflict. CRM/McGraw-Hill, 14 min., color, $195/$20. AD: Teenaged couple engage in a heated argument about the extent of their sexual involvement. Rather stereotyped; wasn't well received by our students.

Young Marriage. CRM/McGraw-Hill, #106670-5, 14 min., color, $195/$20. CD: Shows some problems that occur in early marriage.

Doing It Right (1980). Multi Media, #I 95, 6 min., color, $110/$20. CD: Humorous depiction of a teenage girl as she decides for better or worse to "lose her virginity" and sets out to do it. Addresses such issues as peer pressure and sexual activity, and love vs. sex. Touches on birth control and STDs.

About Sex (1977). Texture, 23 min., color, $290/$35. CD: Addresses a teenage audience and gives factual information on body growth, homosexuality, masturbation, birth control, etc. Can be used in discussion of sex education materials. Blue Ribbon, American Film Festival.

A Three Letter Word for Love (1977). Texture, 27 min., color, $330/$35. CD: Young people from an inner city area talk about various aspects of sex: knowledge, fantasies, experience, and misconceptions. Can be used in discussion of sex education materials.

17

Romance, Sex, and Marriage: All the Guys Ever Want is S.E.X.
(1975). 26 min., color, PSU rental $16.50. CD: Young people
from varying environments describe their experiences and comment
on the meaning and value of sexual relationships. Commentary
by therapist John Brown.

The Sexually Mature Adult (1973). 17 min.,
color, PSU rental $13. AD: Recorded recollections of males
and females of their sexual experiences. Detailed coverage of
sexual response cycle during intercourse through photography of
4 different nude couples and through graphics.

See also Human Sexuality and the Life Cycle (Ch. 14); First
Date (Ch. 6); Who's Doing It? Sexual Attitudes in America
(Ch. 6); Intimacy (Ch. 8); What Guys Want (Ch. 6); Dear
Diary (Ch. 6); Am I Normal? (Ch. 6) and Fathers (Ch. 11).

CHAPTER 16: ADULTHOOD AND AGING

A Ripple of Time (1974). Multi Media, #E 37, 24 min., color,
$330/$50. AD: Interludes of conversation alternate with lovemaking by a 50 year old woman and a 63 year old man. Several
positions are shown, and mutual affection and enjoyment are
obvious. The couple discuss changing self concepts as they
have aged. Our students expressed exhaustion at watching the
duration of the lovemaking and thought that the woman was
atypical of 50 year old women. This film may be more enjoyable
for instructors than for students, but it provides a good
opportunity to discuss stereotypes associated with aging. The
man in the film is none other than the sex researcher Ed Brecher,
who despite his many accomplishments, described (at the eastern
region meeting of the Society for the Scientific Study of Sex
in April, 1983) the film as the project about which he is
most proud.

Not Together Now: End of a Marriage (1975). Polymorph, 25
min., color, $425/$40, PSU rental $16.50. CD: A now-separated
couple discuss their feelings about marriage, their jobs,
their children, and their separation. Avoids the "who is to
blame?" issue, and is helpful in stimulating discussion of the
realities of marriage.

Reflections (1976). Multi Media, #E 53, 25 min., color,
$360/$55. CD: Eight friends share through discussion and
lovemaking their experiences and understandings of group
sexuality. Provides a realistic look at group sex in both
the discussion and actual sexual activities.

Ain't Nobody's Business (1977). Tomato, 52 min., color, rental: $50. AD: This is an acclaimed (25 award or more) documentary on female prosititution. Various women describe their feelings about their work ranging from pride and satisfaction to shame and embarrassment. Good stimulus for discussion of sexual norms and the role of sex in our culture. Our students did not respond particularly positively to this film, complaining that it was overly long, however we had difficulty with the acoustics in the room when we showed it.

Love in Later Life (1982). Multi Media, 30 min., $595/$65. CD: Explicit film about a married couple about 70 years old. They talk about their life together, past and present, and their relationship with each other. They are also depicted in their day to day life, working, making love, etc. Good for stimulating discussion about stereotypes about the sexuality of elderly people.

Hookers (1975). Multi Media, #I 36, 25 min., color, $360/$55. CD: Filmed in collaboration with Margo St. James and COYOTE, this is a controversial depiction of a "working woman's" point of view. Interviews with several women are interspersed with episodes of their meetings with clients.

Coping with Serious Illness: Sexuality (1980). 28 min., color, PSU rental: $25.50. Documentary about Joan Robinson who is dying of cancer and her husband Eric. Focus on the need for love at critical times as well as when there is little stress.

Downhill (1974). Nat'l Film Board of Canada, 36 min., color, PSU rental: $20.50. CD: Middle-aged man on a ski vacation with his girlfriend has heart attack. This emergency necessitates the involvement of his wife and son who thought he was on a business trip.

See also Human Sexuality and the Life Cycle (Ch. 14); Three Styles of Marital Conflict (Ch. 9); Who's Doing it? Sexual Attitudes in America (Introduction); and Sexuality: The Human Heritage (Ch. 14).

CHAPTER 17: SEXUAL PREFERENCE

Coming to Know (1976). Multi Media, #I 21, 10 min., B & W, $215/$35. CD: Two women discuss the development of their identities as lesbians, from early fantasies to first experiences. Feminist politics plays a significant role in their coming out. Their discussion is open without being very explicit.

19

After the Game (1980). Multi Media, #I 90, 19 min., B & W,
$310/$45. CD: A sexually nonexplicit dramatization that
portrays a close and loving relationship between two women
in their early 20s. They identify as heterosexual, but are
beginning to uncover and examine the sexual feelings between
them. Discusses conditioning of male and female gender
roles and emphasizes the importance of honest expression of
sexual feelings.

Pink Triangles (1980). Cambridge, 35 min., color, $650/$108
(week); $65 (2 days); $50 (1 day). If use is limited to one
institution, sale price is $500. CD: Deals with the pre-
judice against lesbians and homosexual males and considers
discrimination, fears, oppression, etc. Synthesizes various
ideas and elements from a number of perspectives.

Susana (1980). Multi Media, #I 91, 24 min., B & W, $330/$50.
CD: This self-portrait documentary is concerned with Susana's
struggle to assert her lesbianism and lifestyle in the face
of her family's disapproval. Film is a general statement on
lesbianism and the problems one may encounter in dealing with
family and friends.

Michael, A Gay Son (1981). Filmaker's, 27 min., color, $450/
$45. CD: Reveals the feelings and needs of Michael, his
parents, and brother and sister on hearing from him that he
is homosexual. The dynamics and difficulties of this family
are shown sympathetically and sensitively. Winner of a number
of awards including the American Film Festival's Blue Ribbon
in 1981.

Closing the Circle (1976). Multi Media, #E 13, 22 min.,
color, $320/$45. CD: Focuses on bisexuality showing a couple
in their 50s spending a sensual afternoon in the country with
a 27 year old friend. The sexual relationship involves humor,
caring, and sensitivity.

Both/And (1975). Multi Media, #E 11, 15 min., color, $260/
$40. CD: Shows a group of nude people discussing their
experiences and how they come to call themselves bisexual.
Considers such issues as monogamy, jealousy, rejection by
both gays and straights, etc. Explicit.

A Gay View/Male (1975). Multi Media, E# 20, 17 min., color,
$280/$40. CD: An intense discussion between three gay men
sharing their sexual attitudes and experiences, feelings
about men, women, children, intimacy, labeling, and acceptance of their homosexuality. Considers some of the games
and roles they were forced to play prior to coming out.

Nick and Jon (1976). Multi Media, 20 min., color, $310/$45.
AD: Depicts a developing gay male affair, with the men discussing their experiences, relationships, lifestyles, and
sexual likes and dislikes. Culminates in an explicit sexual
interaction involving both anal and oral sex, including
momments of humor and affection during the interaction.
This film provides a useful manswer to the question that
some students ask regarding how gays have sex, but we have
shown it only once as we think that it reinforces the stereotype that the primary activity of gays is having sex.

In Winterlight (1974). Multi Media, 18 min., color, $300/$40.
AD: Shows two women as they share their lives and sexuality
together, particularly hand-genital stimulation. Again, we
have shown this film only once, as both women are rather
masculine in appearance which may reinforce the stereotype
that all lesbians are "bull dykes."

What About McBride? (1974). CRM/McGraw-Hill, 10 min., color,
$195/$20, PSU rental: $12. AD: Focuses on the reactions of
two boys to the notion that a friend of theirs may be gay.
We have shown this only once, as our students generally reported that it was below their level of sophistication.

A Woman's Place is in the House (1975). Texture, 28 min.,
color, $350/$45, PSU rental: $17.50. CD: Elaine Nobel,
elected to the Massachusetts House of Representatives, discusses her gayness candidly.

Mixed Marriages: Homosexual Husbands (1977). 14 min., color,
PSU: $250/$45. CD: Despite increased permissiveness, some
homosexuals marry as a "cover" for social or business reasons,
or in some cases, to have children. This 60 Minutes segment,
narrated by Mike Wallace, focuses on what happens when a wife
discovers that her husband is homosexual. Includes interviews
with two mixed marriage families in Great Britain and with the
founder of Sigma Society, a self-help group of women who are
or were married to homosexuals.

See also Self-Loving (Ch. 8); and Sweet Dreams (Ch. 7).

CHAPTER 18:   DISEASES AND DISABILITIES

Women's Health: A Question of Survival (1976). CRM/McGraw-
Hill, #106894-5, 49 min., color, $695/$78, PSU rental: $29.
CD: Investigates the health care women receive including the
administration of potentially dangerous drugs to pregnant
women, questionable masectomies and hysterectomines, and un-
proven methods of birth control.

21

Active Partners (1979). Multi Media, #I 79, 18 min., color, $300/$40. CD: Shows a male quadraplegic and his able-bodied female partner of several years. Moves from nonexplicit to very explicit scenes dealing with the many facets of their relationship including manual, oral, and nongenital sexual stimulation. Each partner discusses the frustrations, concerns, reactions, and adjustments in their relationship. Importance of good communication and a sense of humor is emphasized.

Choices: In Sexuality with Physical Disability (2 parts) (1981). Mercury, Part 1--20 min., $300/$60; Part 2--40 min., color, Both parts, $875/$160 (the distributor will not release Part 2 without Part 1). CD: Part 1 deals primarily with sexual expression after traumatic injury. People are shown dealing with their situations and realize that they remain sexual beings. They discuss their fears, concerns, anxieties, and self-concepts. Part 2 shows explicit scenes to illustrate the possible difficulties, problems, and stimu-lation techniques used by the handicapped. This part is an honest and frank portrayal of sexual activity and relation-ships among the handicapped.

Like Other People (1973). Perennial, #1007, 37 min., color, $442/$52, PSU rental: $18. AD: This is an outstanding film. Physically and/or mentally handicapped people discuss their intense feelings about their relationships. There is a beautiful sequence showing the caring between two palsied lovers, and the film focuses on the complexity of the desire for intimacy and societal (and institutional) concerns re-garding reproduction and contraception. Since first ordering this film a number of years ago, we have ordered it every term and we even remain in the classroom to see it again after having seen it a dozen times or more. Because of the importance of discussing the STDs, and because this film provides one of the most beautiful statements about love that we've ever seen, we often use this film at the end of the term, and it would be very appropriate for the final chapter in our book. Winner of numerous awards, SR: 6.00.

When Love Needs Care. Perennial, 13 min., color, $216/$25. AD: This documentary shows two young people visiting a doctor's office for examination and treatment of an STD. Attempts to debunk myths. SR: 4.60.

You're Not Alone With Herpes (1982). Perennial, 24 min., color. $199 purchase. CD: Focuses on preventing the spread of herpes, and helps sufferers to come to term with herpes and to minimize the symptoms.

See also Coping with Serious Illness: Sexuality (Ch. 16); and Downhill (Ch. 16).

Rape Culture (Updated, 1980). Cambridge, 35 min., color, $525/$106 (1 week); $61 (2 days); $46 (1 day). May also be purchased for $402 if showing is limited to one institution. CD: Establishes the connection between violence and "normal" patterns of male-female interaction and behavior. Explores the elements in our society that contribute to an ideology that supports assault, and includes the perspectives of various social groups.

The Rape Victims (1978). Media Guild, 22 min., color, $395/$38. CD: Documentary narrated by a female rape victim who explores the scope and significance of the increasing prevalence of assault. Particular emphasis is placed on the suffering of the victims. Shows why, where, when, and to whom sexual assault occurs. Demonstrates that assault is violence rather than an expression of sexual feelings.

Incest (1979). Media Guild, 16 min., color, $312/$25. CD: Discusses the reality of incest in our culture. The characters in the film are members of a family, in which the father becomes involved with his 9 year old daughter, and the film records the reactions of other family members as their relationship became known to the rest of the family.

Loved, Honored, and Bruised (1982). Media Guild, 25 min., $445/$40. CD: Shows the experience of a woman who was beaten by her husband during the 13 years of their marriage, but was too ashamed to seek help. Eventually, she leaves with her 5 children to a shelter for battered women. Considers issues of counseling, financial and social support, and legal aid. Interviews with her former spouse show the complexities of this problem.

Incest: The Family Secret. Filmaker's, 57 min., $445/$75. CD: Frank discussion between adult women of their childhood experiences with incest. It is suggested that young women facing this problem become runaways, drug addicts, or prostitutes. Explores the mother's role, families, and presents interviews with fathers in incestuous families.

To Have and To Hold. New Day, 20 min., color, $350/$35. CD: Examines wife abuse from the perspective of men's experience of assaulting their wives, lovers, and girlfriends. Explores personal and societal influences and suggests that the underlying issues involve the socialization of men to use violence to solve problems, control others, etc. Award winner.

Sexual Harassment: A Threat to Your Profits (1981). 19 min.,
color, PSU rental: $25.50. CD: Uses a case study of a woman
employee's charge that her supervisor is guilty of sexual
harassment to trace what should happen at the management level
to deal with such problems. Discusses the definition of sexual
harassment, the negative impact it can have on an organization,
and preventive measures.

Sexual Harassment: That's Not in My Job Description (1981).
19 min., color, PSU rental: $22.50. CD: Case studies of
sexual harassment in the workplace include male, female and
homosexual harassment situations. Discusses preventive measures that can be taken by employees and points out the
difficulty in determining when sexual harassment has taken
place. Gives the Equal Employement Opportunity Commission's
definition of harassment.

Incest: The Victim Nobody Believes (1976). 20 min., color,
PSU rental: $17.50. CD: Examines the extent of child sexual
abuse and points out the impact a childhood incestuous
experience can have through life. In a candid discussion, 3
young men openly discuss what its like to be caught in a web
of fear, confusion, isolation, and guilt.

Why Men Rape (1979). 40 min., color, PSU rental: $25.50.
CD: Interviews with 10 convicted rapists and authorities on
sexual assault indicate that rapists represent a wide variety
of educational, social, and age levels, and that all have in
common a lack of self-esteem. Points out that rape usually
is an act of rage, not of lust, which often has childhood
roots. Includes discussion of acquaintance rapes.

Wife Beating (1976). NBC, 27 min., color, PSU rental: $17.50.
CD: Wife beating, a form of assault that knows no socioeconomic boundaries, is examined from the wife's point of view.
Interviews with battered wives reveal the vicious cycle of
behavior that perpetuates such crimes, the repercussions on
the women themselves and on their children. Suggests possible
remedies. Award winner.

Not A Love Story (197). Nat'l Film Board of Canada. 68 min.,
color. Cost for purchase of 5 year license to show film, $850
or video cassette $450. AD: This excellent documentary pro-
vides footage of the performance of an erotic dancer who
enjoys her work, and then tours the erotic media and performance industry. The topic is treated with more sophistication
than is typical in that there are distinctions made between
erotic materials/performances that are entertaining versus
those that rely on symbolic degradation or victimization of
women for their source of arousal. The film is quite explicit
and impactful. Although the cost is beyond what most of our
departments can afford, several departments may be able to

24

cooperate--particularly if your school has a TV studio--
in obtaining a video cassette.

See also A Film About Sharon (Ch. 7); Dirty Business (Ch. 7);
and Killing Us Softly (Ch. 6).

CHAPTER 20: ATYPICAL SEXUAL ACTIVITY

Radical Sex Styles (1976). Grove Press, 50 min., B & W,
$500/$60. AD: Presents 6 interviews with people discussing
variations in their sexual lifestyles including transvestism,
menage a trois, lesbianism, "promiscuity," bisexuality, and
acting in erotic films. Although we have used this film
several times, it tends to emphasize the "weirdness" of alternative forms of sexual expression.

S-M. Grove Press, Robert Bodenstein, 50 min., B & W. $500/
$50. CD: Documentary on sadomasochism.

See also Auto-Erotic (Ch. 7).

CHAPTER 21: LOVING SEXUAL INTERACTIONS

Love Tapes (1980). Filmaker's, 30 min., B & W, Purchase
only, $25, PSU rental: $18. CD: Shows video tapes made
by diverse people who volunteered to discuss their feelings
about love. Tries to increase the awareness and empathy
of viewers to the needs and feelings of others.

A Long Distance Love Affair (1981). Multi Media, #I 98, 12
min., $200/$30. Comical scenario in which Joe is on a fishing
trip and becomes convinced that his girlfriend is seeing
other men. He decides to return home, and on the way, his
thoughts become increasingly bizarre and he gets quite frenzied.
Useful to stimulate discussion on relationships, jealousy,
trust, etc.

Kinds of Love. Indiana University, 29 min., B & W. Describes
various kinds of love, mistaken ideas about love, and the relationship between love and sex.

Love Story (1975). Media Guild, 20 min., color, $395/$30.
CD: Media treatment of heterosexual relationships is con-
trasted with possible alternative treatments.

See also Sexual Values: A Matter of Responsibility (Ch. 1);
Like Other People (Ch. 18); and Love and the Art of Sexual
Fulfillment (Ch. 8).

FILM DISTRIBUTORS

Cambridge Documentary Films, Inc., P.O. Box 385, Cambridge,
    MA   02139 (617-354-3677)

CRM/McGraw-Hill, P.O. Box 641, Del Mar, CA   92014 (714-453-5000).

Document Associates, Inc., 880 Third Ave., New York, NY   10022,
    (212-593-1647).

Filmaker's Library, Inc., 133 E. 58th St., New York, NY   10022

Focus International, Inc., 333 W. 52nd St., New York, NY   10019
    (212-586-8612).

Grove Press Films, 196 W. Houston St., New York, NY   10014
    (212-242-4900).

Human Relations Media, 175 Tomkins Ave., Pleasantville, NY
    10570 (800-431-2050; in NY or Canada, collect, 914-769-
    7496).

Kinsey Institute for Sex Research, Indiana University,
    Bloomington, IN

The Media Guild, 11526 Sorrento Valley Rd., Suite J. San Diego,
    CA   92121.

Mercury Productions, 17 W. 45th St., New York, NY   10035.

Multi-Media Resource Center, 1525 Franklin St., San Francisco,
    CA   94109 (415-673-5100).

New Day Film Co-op, Inc., P.O. Box 315, Franklin Lakes, NJ
    07417 (201-891-8240).

National Film Board of Canada, 16th Floor, 1251 Avenue of the
    Americas, New York, NY   10020-1173.

Perennial Education, 477 Roger Williams, P.O. Box 855, Ravinia,
    Highland Park, IL   60036 (800-323-9084; in IL, call collect
    312-433-1610).

Polymorph Films, 118 South Street, Boston, MA   02111   (617-542-
    2004).

PSU.   Audio-Visual Services.   The Pennsylvania State University,
    University Park, PA   16802   (814-865-6314).

Research Press, Box 3177Y, Champaign, IL   61821   (217-352-
    3273).

Texture Films, Inc., 1600 Broadway, New York, NY   10019   (212-
    586-6960).

Time-Life Video, 100 Eisenhower Dr., P.O. Box 644, Paramus, NY
    07652

Tomato Productions, Inc., P.O. Box 1235, Evergreen, CO   80439
    (303-838-6426).

PART 2: SUGGESTIONS FOR CLASS TIME ACTIVITIES

GENERAL RECOMMENDATIONS

We will offer suggestions to correspond with each chapter, but
in preparation for the course, we have some recommendations that
may be useful throughout the course. These include names and
addresses of publications to provide the latest sex research
findings, and a sexual attitudes and behavior questionnaire that
may be administered at the beginning of the term so that average
responses of students in the course can be provided where relevant throughout the course.

You may also wish to skim the rest of Part 2 for suggestions
for guest panels, speakers, etc., as they generally need to be
contacted well in advance of the specific day on which they
come to class.

RESOURCES

Your college library may subscribe to some of the following
journals. If they do not, you may want to consider asking them
to do so, although we find it useful to have a personal subscription to the following journals for lecture preparation, in
addition to asking our library to subscribe for the use of students. The prices and addresses listed are current as we go to
press with the Instructor's Guide (11/83).

SIECUS Reports. This is a journal published by the Sex Information and Education Council of the United States, founded by
Mary Calderone, M.D. It is published bimonthly and distributed
to SIECUS Associate Members who pay annual fees of $40. Library
fee is also $40. SIECUS Reports publishes articles reporting
overviews of research, book and audio-visual reviews, various
resources available for sexuality educators, descriptions of
current controversies over sex education, proposed regulations,
etc. Some of their articles can provide the basis for an entire
lecture. Subscriptions may be obtained by writing to SIECUS,
80 Fifth Ave., Suite 801-2, New York, NY 10011.

The Journal of Sex Research (JSR). JSR is published by the
Society for the Scientific Study of Sex, Inc. four times a year.
It contains reports of empirical research on sexuality, book reviews, announcements of upcoming meetings, etc. It focuses
primarily on social-psychological studies, and may be obtained
for $35 (library rate $55); or as a part of the membership dues
in the Society for the Scientific Study of Sex (SSSS) which are
$60 a year. SSSS holds several scientific meetings a year for
the presentation of research and workshops relevant to sex educa-

tion, therapy and research. To obtain information, a subscription or SSSS membership (which provides one with four newsletters a year and the programs for the annual meetings), write to SSSS, P.O. Box 29797, Philadelphia, PA 19117.

Archives of Sexual Behavior (ASB). This journal is published every other month and contains reports of empirical research on biological studies of atypical patterns of sexual behavior as well as some social-psychological studies. It is available for $48 a year from Plenum Publishing Company, P.O. Box, 730 Canal Street Station, New York, NY 10013.

Planned Parenthood Federation of America (PP). There are a variety of resources available from PP and from their research wing, the Alan Guttmacher Institute (AGI). We suggest writing to them (810 Seventh Ave., New York, NY 10019) for a list of current resources. AGI publishes Family Planning Perspectives, a journal that publishes research relevant to reproduction, contraception, and birth control. They tend to publish research based on nationally representative samples of the Kantner & Zelnik sort rather than that based on small local samples, and the journal is an invaluable source of the latest information on the benefits and risks associated with various contraceptive and abortion methods. PP also publishes the Public Affairs Newsletter which provides information on legislation being considered at both national and state levels. The newsletter frequently contains copies of debate published in the Congressional Record, as well as information on international events relevant to the general issues of reproduction and birth control.

Additional journals of a more specialized nature, as described in Box 3-1 in Chapter 3 include Journal of Homosexuality; Alternative Lifestyles; Journal of Sex Education and Therapy; Journal of Sex and Marital Therapy. Psychology Abstracts publishes a section devoted to gender roles and sexuality which provides a source of recent research in a variety of different journals. Finally, articles relevant to human sexuality appear occasionally in the mainstream journals in the various disciplines to which those of us teaching the course belong.

For group discussion and values clarification exercises, see Kaplan, L. B., et al. Group Strategies in Understanding Human Sexuality: Getting in Touch, Dubuque, IA: Wm. C. Brown, 1978, and Morrison & Price, Values in Sexuality, New York: Hart, 1974.

INSTRUCTIONS: SEXUAL ATTITUDES AND EXPERIENCES QUESTIONNAIRE

We have included a large number of questions to give to your
students that may be relevant to present at various points in
the course, but you probably should select particular items
that you think would be of interest to you and/or your students
rather than administering the entire questionnaire, as it would
take quite a bit of time to respond to the entire instrument.

IMPORTANT: Most professional organizations have ethical guidelines governing the conduct of research, and most colleges
have committees that review research instruments and the conditions under which they are administered. Because the following questionnaire contains items that tap very personal areas,
we would advise submitting whatever portions (if any) of this
questionnaire you wish to administer to your college committee
for approval prior to administration. This protects both
students and faculty. In addition, the form itself does not
request any information that would personally identify students,
nor do we ever ask students to provide personal sexual histories
with their names or other identifying information attached to
them.

Unless you are able to provide sufficient space in your classroom so that students are not able to glance at each other's
responses while they are making them, you will probably have
to distribute the questionnaire for them to complete at home
and return to class at a later date. Keeping track of the
number of people who receive versus return the questionnaire
can provide you with the nonresponse rate which you can discuss
when considering possible sources of bias in the sex research
chapter (3).

SEXUAL ATTITUDES AND EXPERIENCES QUESTIONNAIRE

Instructions: Write your answer in the blank to the left.

DEMOGRAPHIC BACKGROUND

____Gender: a. male; b. female
____Age (in years)
____Class: a. fresh.; b. soph.; c. jr.; d. sr.; e. other
____Religious training: a. Protestant; b. Catholic; c. Jewish;
____d. Atheist/Agnostic; e. Other (specify_____)
____Frequency of attendance at religious services per year.
____Political affiliation: a. Conservative; b. Democrat;
____c. Independent; d. Liberal; e. Republican
_____Approximate family income annually

ATTITUDES

Instructions: Place the letter representing one of these 5 responses to indicate how you feel about the following issues relevant to sexuality:

a. strongly approve
b. approve somewhat
c. neutral
d. disapprove somewhat
e. strongly disapprove

____1. Education about sexuality in the public schools.
____2. Availability of non-prescription contraceptives (condom, foam, vaginal sponge) in vending machines in public restrooms.
____3. Sexual intercourse between an engaged couple.
____4. Sexual intercourse between a couple when they are in love.
____5. Sexual intercourse between a couple when they have dated a couple of times.
____6. Sexual intercourse by a woman with a man the same night she meets him.
____7. Sexual intercourse by a man with a woman the same night he meets her.
____8. Sexual relations between two women.
____9. Sexual relations between two men.
____10. Masturbation by a single person who has no sexual partner.
____11. Masturbation by a single person whose partner is unavailable (lives out of town, etc.)
____12. Masturbation by a married person.
____13. Oral-genital sexual contact.
____14. Abortion when a woman is pregnant due to rape or incest, or when her health is endangered.
____15. Abortion when a woman requests it for whatever reasons.

_____16. Group sex (sexual relations between three or more con-
senting partners).
_____17. Mate exchange (couples exchanging partners for purposes
of sexual relations).
_____18. Wives taking primary care of children while husband
works.
_____19. Husband taking primary care of children while wife
works.
_____20. Legal availability of erotic materials (books, movies,
magazines, etc.) for adults.

EXPERIENCES

For the following questions please indicate the age at which
you first had the following experiences. If you did not have
the experience, please write N/A (not applicable) on the line.

_____1. Discussion with mother about names for genitals.
_____2. Discussion with father about names for genitals.
_____3. Discussion with mother about menstrual process.
_____4. Discussion with father about menstrual process.
_____5. Discussion with mother about nocturnal orgasm.
_____6. Discussion with father about nocturnal orgasm.
_____7. Discussion with mother about fertilization (sperm meets
egg).
_____8. Discussion with father about fertilization.
_____9. Discussion with mother about emotional aspects ("love")
of sexual intimacy
_____10. Discussion with father about emotional aspects of
sexual intimacy.
_____11. Discussion with mother about passionate aspects (sexual
arousal) of sexual intimacy.
_____12. Discussion with father about passionate aspects of
sexual intimacy.
_____13. Discussion with friends of same gender about sex.
_____14. Discussion of friends of other gender about sex.
_____15. Playing "doctor" (looking at, touching, each other's
genitals) with friends of same gender.
_____16. Playing "doctor" with friends of other gender.
_____17. Age (in years and months) of first menstrual period.
_____18. Age (in years and months) of first nocturnal orgasm.
_____19. Awareness of feelings of sexual arousal toward someone
of the same gender.
_____20. Awareness of feelings of sexual arousal toward someone
of the other gender.
_____21. Kissing someone of the same gender.
_____22. Kissing someone of the other gender.
_____23. Genital stimulation with someone of the same gender.
_____24. Genital stimulation with someone of the other gender.
_____25. Orgasm with someone of the same gender.
_____26. Orgasm with someone of the other gender.

31

_____27. Sexual intercourse (penile-vaginal penetration) with
someone of the other gender.
_____28. Recieving oral genital stimulation.
_____29. Giving oral genital stimulation.
_____30. Self stimulation (masturbation).
_____31. Receiving anal stimulation.
_____32. Giving anal stimulation.
_____33. Used a method of contraception. (specify method_____)
_____34. Regularly used a method of contraception (specify
method_____)
_____35. Experienced a pregnancy (by self or partner).

For the following please fill in the blank:

_____1. Number of sexual partners in life of other gender.
_____2. Number of sexual partners in life of same gender.
_____3. Frequency (per month) of masturbation.
_____4. Frequency (per month) of sexual relations with a partner.
_____5. Number of unwanted pregnancies by self or partner.
_____6. Number of pregnancies (see #5) resolved by
        _____a. keeping baby
        _____b. giving baby up for adoption
        _____c. miscarriage
        _____d. abortion
_____7. Age at which you would like, ideally, to marry or to
make a long-term commitment to someone. If you don't
wish to make a long-term commitment (marital or other-
wise), write N/A.
_____8. Age at which you would like, ideally, to have a child.
If you don't wish to have children, write N/A.
_____9. Age at which you first saw erotic books or magazines.
_____10. Likelihood that you would force someone to have sex
if you could be sure that you would not be caught.
        a. none
        b. slightly likely
        c. somewhat likely
        d. likely
        e. very likely
_____11. Have you ever tried to force someone to have sex who
didn't want to?
_____12. Have you ever forced someone to have sex who didn't
want to?
_____13. Has anyone ever tried to force you to have sex when
you didn't want to?
_____14. Has anyone ever forced you to have sex when you didn't
want to?

CHAPTER 1: PERCEPTIONS OF SEXUALITY:
HISTORICAL AND CROSS-CULTURAL OVERVIEW

Topics covered in Chapter

I. Difficulties for interpreting historical practices, using
rationalizations for circumcision as an example, beginnings
of Western civilization, early religious influences, Mesopotamia,
box on worship of the Great Mother, matriarchy and patriarchy,
ambivalence about women as dangerous versus able to create new
life, Egypt, Judaism, Greece, Rome.

II. Christianity, box on Jimmy Carter's "lust" interview in
Playboy, body/soul dichotomy. Beliefs about men versus women,
same-gender relationships, etc., are discussed for these
periods.

III. The medieval period, courtly love, homosexuality, witch-
craft, box on contemporary beliefs in demons, views on purposes
of marriage, attitudes toward sexual variations, box on marriage and prostitution in 15th-century France.

IV. Victorianism and variations in sexual behavior, religious
versus increasing role of science as influence on sexual ideas,
description of contributions of Krafft-Ebing, Havelock Ellis,
Freud, box on clitoral-vaginal orgasm debate.

Use of Class Time

First Class. This chapter is not assigned until the second
class session, and we spend the first class session introducing
the course, ourselves, and our background preparation for
teaching the course. We point out that most people who teach
human sexuality have been trained in one of the traditional
social or biological sciences disciplines as there are still
only a few doctoral programs available for people who wish to
obtain an advanced degree in human sexuality.

A discussion of the difference between moral values and
scientific evidence can be introduced here. For those of you
using this book, you may want to point out that the book (and
probably your course) is not aimed at shaping their morality,
but rather on increasing their sophistication in understanding
new findings about sexuality and on making decisions. The
emphasis is not on sex education but on increasing their
knowledge about determinants of sexual attitudes and behaviors,
consequences of various choices, and the ability to evaluate
sex research that is reported long after they are no longer
enrolled in the course.

You may want to administer portions of the questionnaire provided above, or the Sexual Knowledge Survey (in the book) or
both, at this point.

Second Class. After they have read Ch. 1, an overview of the
variations in beliefs about particular sexual behaviors can be
helpful to make the point that our contemporary beliefs feel
"natural," but other belief systems have seemed as natural to
people living in other times. In lecture, we move historically
through five major topics--the nature of male sexuality (easily
elicited); female sexuality (ranging from insatiable to very
difficult to elicit); homosexual relations (the highest form
of companionship to evidence of sin and mental illness); sexual
assault (partially due to female as temptress versus male as
expressing dominance needs because of low self-esteem); and
masturbation (sin, then sickness needing surgery and therapy,
now either neutral or a positive release and source of information about one's sexual responses). The point of this is to
show the diversity of beliefs about sexuality at different
points in time. Chapter 1 presents these and other topics
chronologically. Presentation of these issues topically can
be helpful in making the overall point.

A discussion of the historical roots of the mind-body dichotomy
and its contemporary manifestations in our religious institutions would also be appropriate here.

We have shown the film Mammalian Sexual Behavior, then asked
students to define "sex," and the onset of human sexuality.
After asking for some of their definitions, the difference in
opinions of experts can be discussed. Specifically, Mary
Calderone suggests that we are sexual beings throughout life
(see Ch. 5 for her data on prenatal sexual responses), whereas
the sociologist John Gagnon maintains that sexuality involves
cognitive interpretations, and until we label and define events,
our responses, etc., as sexual (as influenced by our culture),
we are not really sexual beings.

Recent Research. Bixler, Sibling incest in the royal families
of Egypt, Peru, and Hawaii, JSR, 1982, 18, 264-281; Haeberle,
The Jewish contribution to the development of sexology, JSR,
1982, 18, 305-323; Money & Davison, Adult penile circumcision:
Erotosexual and cosmetic sequelae, JSR, 1983, 19, 289-292;
Greer et al., A technique for foreskin reconstruction and some
preliminary results, JSR, 1982, 18, 324-330; Mohl & Greer,
Letter to editor, ASB, 1983, 12, 275-276.

CHAPTER 2:   CONTEMPORARY EXPLANATIONS OF HUMAN SEXUALITY

Topics Covered in Chapter

I. Social learning approaches, box on the wild boy of Aveyron,
how learning processes affect sexuality, classical and instrumental conditioning, social learning theory, symbolic interaction.

II. Psychoanalytic approaches, box on Freud's life, Freud's
theory of personality development, id, ego, superego, box on
a study date using psychoanalytic interpretations of the
interaction, infantile sexuality, psychosexual stages with
discussion of the Oedipal and Electra complexes, box on the
myth of Oedipus, discussion of contemporary standing of Freud's
ideas, recent psychoanalytic developments.

III. Evolutionary approaches, Sagan's compression of the 15
billion year lifespan of the universe into a single calendar
year, sociobiological explanations of homosexuality and gender
differences in sexual strategies, discussion of the confusion
between theories, politics, and morality.

Use of Class Time. We generally allot two class sessions to
a discussion of theories. Students can be asked at the end of
the previous class to describe several aspects of sexuality
that they would like to see explained. The instructor can then
pick a couple of these—for example, differences in male-female
sexual assertiveness, or same gender sexual relations—and
describe the assumptions underlying each of the theoretical
approaches in their explanations of observed variations in
sexuality.

One of the sociobiological films can be shown, as this is
generally the theoretical approach with which students are
least familiar. The film with Wilson and Lewontin provides
a good example of how people confuse theories, politics,
and religion.

Recent Research. Reiss, Trouble in paradise, JSR, 1982, 18,
97-113; Money, Sexosophy: A new concept, JSR, 1982, 18, 364-
366.

CHAPTER 3: RESEARCH ON SEXUALITY

Topics Covered in Chapter

I. The sex research process, box on journals that publish sex research, box on anxiety over learning about research methods.

    A. Definition of research terms, sampling issues and sources of bias, box on Paul Robinson's review of Hite's books.

    B. Research methods, advantages and disadvantages of correlational vs. experimental methods, box on descriptive vs. inferential statistics, field vs. lab. research, box on field research with preliterate tribe, cross-sectional vs. longitudinal research.

    C. Measurement issues, self administered questionnaires, surveys, and scales, box on development of sexual knowledge survey including coverage of concepts of reliability and validity, interviews, direct observation in lab and field settings, physiological response measures including plethysmographs and thermography, biochemical response measures including discussion of issues of reliability in hormone assays and the conclusions that may be drawn, case study approach as source of hypotheses but not generalizable, comparison of the advantages and disadvantages of each approach.

II. Evaluating results of sex research with discussion of generalizability using timing of administration of DES as example, potential side effects using thalidomide, temporary vs. lasting effects using Hawthorne effect and changing partners to solve problems, and replication.

III. The impact of ethics, societal beliefs, and politics on sex research. Discussion of ethics includes descriptions of problems associated with Laud Humphreys' research and studies of side effects of contraceptives, principles of risk-benefit and informed consent. Social and political issues are raised in the context of rejection of love and sex as appropriate topics for research, box on Proxmire's Golden Fleece award.

Use of Class Time. A chronological review of the history of attempts to get information about sexuality in our century can underline the reasons why we still have relatively little information about a number of aspects about sexuality. Background information for such a lecture may be found in Bullough (in press, 1983), Byrne (1977), and Magoun (1981). The Bullough article reviews the influence of funding by the Rockefeller foundation and others on sex research, asserting that biologi-

cal studies were more popular projects for the receipt of
funding than were studies focusing on social-psychological
bases of sexual attitudes and behavior. As we go to press,
it is scheduled to be published in an upcoming issue of the
Journal of Sex Research, but you might want to write to
historian V. Bullough, Ph.D. (Dean, Faculty of Natural &
Social Sciences, SUNY-Buffalo, 1300 Elmwood Ave., Buffalo, NY
14222) for that article, plus a copy of his presidential
address to SSSS, Nov., 1983, "The Problems of Doing Research
in a Delicate Field." The article by social psychologist
D. Byrne is superb for lecture material, discussing the fact
that our early information came from animals, natives, and
crazies, with lots of examples. That article and the Magoun
article are both referenced in the text. Magoun describes
the early work on sexual response by J. B. Watson with photos
of some of the instruments he used to measure physiological
responses. Problems faced by others including O. H. Mowrer
and Kinsey are also discussed in this JSR article.

The film showing Wardell Pomeroy collecting a sex history
might also be shown.

Recent Research. Hudson et al., "A short-form scale to measure
liberal vs. conservative orientations toward human sexual
expression, JSR, 1983, 19, 258-272; Levitt, Estimating the duration of sexual behavior: A laboratory analog study, ASB,
1983, 12, 329-335; Davidson et al., Maintenance of sexual
function in a castrated man treated with ovarian steriods,
ASB, 1983, 12, 263-274; Beck et al., Operating characteristics
of the vaginal photoplethysmograph: Some implications for its
use, ASB, 1983, 12, 43-58.

CHAPTER 4:   SEXUAL ANATOMY AND PHYSIOLOGY

Topics Covered in the Chapter

I.   Sexual Anatomy

    A.   The male sexual system including the testes with a box
on self-examination of the testicles, genital ducts, the source
and composition of semen with discussion of reactions to
swallowing semen during oral sex, and the penis with a review
of research showing that penis length is irrelevant to female
sexual pleasure.

    B.   The female sexual system including the ovaries,
fallopian tubes, uterus, vagina, Grafenberg spot with a box
showing how to find it, vulva, labia, pelvic muscle with a box
on Kegel exercises, breasts with a box on self-exams, and the
lips with a discussion of cross-cultural variations in attitudes
toward kissing.

II. The nervous system and sympathetic and parasympathetic divisions, central nervous system, spinal cord and pudendal and pelvic nerves, and structures in the brain relevant to sexual response.

III. Hormones and the endocrine system, adrenal and pituitary glands with a box defining major sex hormones, the phases of the menstrual cycle with a box describing a positive response to menarche.

Use of Class Time. We generally devote two class sessions to this topic, going over the material on anatomy and physiology in some detail, as this tends to be difficult for students to assimilate. The transpariencies of male and female genital and reproductive structures can be used to discuss sexual response and the structures contributing to it. The relative absence of nerve endings in the inner two-thirds of the vagina can be discussed with its relevance to female sexual response, and the Grafenberg spot along with the latest research on it can be described.

We strongly recommend showing the film Miracle of Life, which has gotten the highest student rating of any film we've shown, at the conclusion of the discussion of anatomy as students are in a better position to understand what they are seeing. The Orgasmic Expulsion film, showing the location and stimulation of the Grafenberg spot, is also effective here, and although some of our students think it is "too explicit," others find it extremely interesting.

CHAPTER 5: PRENATAL DEVELOPMENT AND GENDER DIFFERENTIATION

Topics Covered in Chapter

I. Fertilization, cells, chromosomes, genes, sex chromosomes and genetic gender, box on greater vulnerability of males than females to various disorders.

II. Prenatal development, the germinal and embryonic stages, gender differentiation, gonadal gender with box on research on the effects of hormones on brain structures, genital gender, the fetal stage with a month-by-month description of development until birth.

III. Atypical prenatal development, chromosomal abnormalities with box on Down's syndrome, and table showing the correlation of maternal age to incidence, sex chromosomal abnormalities, Klinefelter's XYY, Turner's, and triple X syndromes, and amniocentesis, inconsistencies in prenatal gender differentiation and the role of hormones during the process.

<u>Use of Class Time</u>. In the discussion of Down's syndrome and
other chromosomal abnormalities, we discuss the new research
on the potential contribution by the father. There is an
opportunity here to talk about the potential interaction of
social factors with biological "facts", however, that we do
not discuss in the book, as there has not been enough time to
accumulate data relevant to our speculation. That is, we
speculate that the strong correlation between maternal age
and Down's syndrome, show in Table 5-1 (p. 139) will diminish
in modern industrialized countries in the next few decades.
Specifically, throughout most of the history of our species,
it was expected that women would become pregnant within a
decade or so of reaching reproductive maturity. This strong
norm with respect to the centrality of women's reproductive
role would mean that those women who had not had children by
the age of 30 or 35 had some difficulty leading to low
fertility or miscarriages. These difficulties could also
contribute to the incidence of birth defects among older
women when they finally were able to get pregnant and carry
a child to birth. The shift toward postponing birth among
women who wish to complete their educations and/or establish
their careers, however, means that the pool of older women
giving birth for the first time will include a larger proportion of women who could have become pregnant without
difficulty in their early 20s had they chosen to do so. If
our analysis based on this social factor is accurate, we
should see a decrease in the likelihood of having children
with birth defects among older women in the next few decades,
at least in industralized countries or among women who
deliberately choose to postpone pregnancy.

When amniocentesis is discussed in Ch. 5, you may want to
contrast it with the newly developed technique, chorionic
villi sampling. This is not discussed in the book, as we
weren't aware of the technique until after the book was in
press. In describing it, it may be helpful to define a few
terms on a transparency or blackboard:
     Chorion: the lay of tissue that surrounds the embryo
during the first two months; later develops into the placenta.
     Villi: finger-like projections of tissue that transfer
oxygen, nutrients, and waste between mother and embyro.
     The process involves insertion of a long thin tube into
the uterus via the vagina, then positioning it (with the help
of sonography) between the lining of the uterus and the
chorion. About half a dozen villi are suctioned into the
tube; these villi contain fetal embyronic cells that can be
analyzed for the presence of genetic defects. The sample can
be obtained as early as the 5th week of pregnancy (as
compared to having to wait until the onset of the second
trimester with amniocentesis), and if evidence of genetic
problems are found, the woman may obtain an abortion at six
to eight weeks. The procedure may be performed in a doctor's

office at a cost of about $550 to $800, and it is expected
that the procedure will be widely available in a short period
of time. In fact, it may be available in your community by
the time you read this; a call to the local medical society
may provide you with that information. Risks are expected to
be no greater than those with amniocentesis. Early detection
may also increase the chances of intervening surgically with
the fetus in time to correct difficulties arising from
genetic defects before the fetus has been damaged.

In both chapters 5 and 6, we are attempting to show the com-
plexity of the gender variables. In our own lectures, we
introduce this set of chapters with a transparency discussing
the eight variables of gender:
    Genetic gender: Possession of XX or XY chromosomes,
determined at conception.
    Gonadal gender: Differentiation of ovaries or testes.
    Hormonal gender: Secretion of relatively larger amounts
of masculinizing or femininizing hormones.
    Genital gender: Differentiation of the internal and
external reproductive/sexual organs.
    Assigned gender: Labeling of a newborn as "boy" or "girl."
    Gender identity: Sense of being male or female.
    Gender roles: Expected traits and behaviors of people as
a function of their gender in a given culture.
    Gender role identification: Extent to which an individual
incorporates the traits and behaviors associated with masculinity
and or femininity in a given culture.

We then go through each of these variables describing typical
development as each variable manifests itself, and atypical
development that can occur. We label the first four as "biological" variables and the last four as "socio-psychological"
variables. We also point out that people frequently confuse
preference for people of the same gender as gender identity
disorders, noting that homosexual, bisexual, or heterosexual
preference is independent of these variables of gender.

CHAPTER 6:   GENDER IDENTITIES AND GENDER ROLES

Topics Covered in Chapter

I. Definitions of the social and psychological variables of
gender including assigned gender, gender identity, gender roles,
and gender role identification.

II. Gender and parental treatment, gender differences in
infancy, gender role socialization, contemporary explanations
of gender differences, gender role identity, androgyny and
psychological health.

III. Transsexuality (TS), definition, incidence, male-to-female and female-to-male TS and gender reassignment, controversies about TS including diagnoses, explanations, and appropriate "treatment," (surgery or psychotherapy?).

IV. Transvestism (TV), definition, incidence, boxes on Virginia Prince's fairy tale analogy, "color typing" and on diagnostic criteria for transvestism and gender identity disorders, clinical vs. nonclinical samples of TV, explanations, box on transvestism among scorpion flies.

Use of Class Time. Our inclusion of TS and TV in this chapter on gender identity and roles is very different from the usual organization found in sex texts. As noted in the last chapter of this guide, we treat chapters 5 and 6 as a unit for an examination of the variables of gender, and chapter 6 focuses on the social and psychological gender variables.

If you live in or near a large urban area, you may be able to find a group of female impersonators (FPs) who would be willing to speak on a panel about their feelings about gender. Prior to their appearance, you might ask students to write down questions they would like to ask the FPs so that you can give these questions to the panel. It is interesting that we have no bars headlining male impersonators, and you might ask students (and the panel) why they think that is.

Alternatively, we sometimes take interested students on a "fieldtrip" to a female impersonator show.

The Bem's Sex Role Inventory (1974), or the Personal Attributes Questionnaire (Spence, Helmreich, & Stapp, 1972) can be given to students to demonstrate the qualities that are considered typical of masculinity and femininity. In showing students how to score these measures, it is important to remind them that gender identity is independent of sexual preference for same or other gender partners.

Recent Research. Korman & Leslie, The relationship of feminist ideology and date expense sharing to perceptions of sexual aggression in dating, JSR, 1982, 18, 114-129; Bullough et al., A comparative study of male transvestites, male-to-female transsexuals, and male homosexuals, JSR, 1983, 19, 238-257; Coleman, R. O. Acoustic correlates of speaker sex identification: Implications for the transsexual voice, JSR, 1983, 19, 293-306; Leitenberg & Slavin, Comparison of attitudes toward transsexuality and homosexuality, ASB, 1983, 12, 237-246; Levine & Shumaker, Increasingly Ruth: Toward understanding sex reassignment, ASB, 1983, 12, 247-261; Blanchard & Steiner, Gender reorientation, psychological adjustment, and involvement with female partners in female to male transsexuals, ASB, 1983, 12, 149-157.

CHAPTER 7:   SEXUAL AROUSAL, FANTASIES, AND FEELINGS

Topics Covered in Chapter

I.   Learning to be aroused, mechanisms of classical and
instrumental conditioning of arousal to stimuli, Berscheid
& Walter's two-stage model of "love," (actually, infatuation).

II.   Sources of arousal, including touch, smell, sight, etc.
Discussion of visual erotica, "pornography," legal issues,
and the findings of the Commission on Obscenity and
Pornography regarding erotica (note that these findings are
limited to nonviolent erotica--violent erotica is discussed
in Ch. 19), and the use of children in erotic material.
Discussion of kissing as involving many of our senses,
and its sexual and nonsexual uses in included, as is a
review of findings regarding "aphrodisiacs" and "anaphrodisiacs."

III.   Variations in response to feelings of arousal (enjoyment vs. guilt), purposes of arousal with a discussion of
potential importance of sexual bonding beyond simply conceiving and how such bonding may be beneficial to our species
given the relatively lengthy period of time required for
human offspring to become self sufficient.   Discussion of
interpretations of arousal by children and adolescents and
the availability (or nonavailability) of information about
arousal, particularly for young females.   Description of
socialization to feel guilty about sexual feelings, gender
differences and similarities in reported arousal, differences
in findings from survey vs. lab research regarding males and
females.

IV.   Fantasy and sexual arousal, media conditioning of arousal
to specific stimuli, discussion of psychological evaluation
of the deviance (early) or normalcy (contemporary) of sexual
fantasies, speculations regarding the functions of sexual
fantasies.

Use of Class Time.   We think that the topic covered in this
chapter is a major reason for student enrollment.   Office hour
visits   by students in the course, in our experience, generally involve one of three major issues: do you think I'm
pregnant? do I have an STD, and am I crazy because I'm
thinking about ---?   For the first two, we refer them to
Planned Parenthood or physicians for diagnosis.   For the
later, we try to reinforce points made in the book and in
lecture.   Despite beliefs that dominate our culture and our
religious institutions to the contrary, thoughts and actions
are very different.   In lecture, we talk about thoughts--
fantasies--of eliminating rivals for our partners, siblings,

parents, our partners when their behavior is a source of pain to us, etc. There is, however, a huge difference between thinking about this and carrying out the behavior. We remind them of the trouncing Jimmy Carter got when he talked about his thoughts (lusting after women) even though he acknowledged no behavior with women other than his spouse. We ask them to think about the scariest movie they've seen (we used to use Psycho, but also, like memories of what you were doing when Kennedy was shot, this example dates us!) and to think about their success in banishing the frightening images and fears from the movie if they are trying to go to sleep alone later. The overall point is that it is extraordinarily difficult to control one's thoughts, but that one's thoughts don't affect the wellbeing of others unless they are translated to behavior. That being the case, there is no point in feeling guilty about socially disapproved sexual thoughts (fantasies); in fact, if the thoughts are pleasant, one can simply enjoy them with impunity! We suggest that fantasies can be a valuable source of information about the range of alternative behaviors one can select, and for which one is willing to take responsibility, etc. The overall point is that we can control our behavior and we are responsible for our choices, but we can't control our thoughts; when they are unpleasant, we have to suffer through; when they are pleasant, why not enjoy them?

We begin this class with an exercise. We ask students to raise their hands if they've ever known anyone they thought was emotionally disturbed. Most of the students raise their arms. We then ask them to describe the traits and behaviors that led them to the inference of emotional disturbance. These are listed on the board or on a transparency labeled "Emotional Disturbance." Students generally list such things as mood shifts, irritability, inability to concentrate, nonreliability, obsessions, etc. We then cross out "Emotional Disturbance" and write "In Love" in its place. As students read through the list they have generated, there is a lot of laughter. This can be discussed in the context of the difference between infatuation (a feeling or set of fantasies) and decisions about behavior. This exercise can also be used when students read the final chapter.

The film "Orange" can be shown as an example of the variety of objects that can be perceived erotically.

Recent Research. Gillman & Lichtigfeld, The effects of nitrous oxide and naloxone on orgasm in human females, JSR, 1983, 19, 49-57; Abramson & Mechanic, Sex and the media: Three decades of best-selling books and major motion pictures, ASB, 1983, 12, 185-206; Malatesta et al., Acute alcohol intoxication and female orgasmic response, JSR, 1982, 18, 1-17.

CHAPTER 8:   SEXUAL BEHAVIOR

Topics Covered in Chapter

I.   Sources of sexual pleasure, self-stimulation, gender differences in masturbatory techniques, manual stimulation, oral
sex and stimulation techniques, with box on the legality of
various sexual activities, coital positions including man
above, woman above, side by side, and rear entry, anal intercourse, discussion of the various motives for engaging in
sexual stimulation and the difficulties associated with pre-
occupation with achieving simultaneous orgasm.

II.   The sexual response cycle, physical reactions during
excitement, plateau, orgasm, and resolution, variations in
sexual response patterns, box on Vance & Wagner's male and
female descriptions of orgasm, Kaplan's three phases of
sexual response.

III.   Orgasm controversies, variations in female orgasmic
patterns, vulval, uterine, and blended orgasm, box on evolution and female orgasm, research on female ejaculation, the
consistency of male vs. female orgasm, multiple orgasm in
females and males.

Use of Class Time.   We find a certain amount of redundancy
with material presented in the chapter on physiological
responses to sexual stimulation helpful to students.   Emphasis
on enormous variation in sexual appetites, across and within
people, can help to reduce students' tendency to compare themselves with "average" responses, and we use food analogies
("sometimes you want a quickie--hamburger & soda, other times
its fun to linger over a 7 course meal, and both are 'normal'").

The material on female ejaculation in the book references
everything presented or published on the topic through October,
1983, but students are very interested in the topic, so you
may want to search for any later publications.   The orgasmic
expulsion film may be shown here appropriately if you haven't
shown it earlier.

The Sexually Mature Adult film may be shown here; we think
it is very good for demonstrating variations in responses,
but students complain that the hairstyles and clothing make
it dated, and we are looking for a more recent film with
the same general coverage.

Recent Research.   deRosset Myers et al., Dimensions of female
sexuality: A factor analysis, ASB, 1983, 12, 159-166;
Frauman, The relationship between physical exercise, sexual
activity, and desire for sexual activity, JSR, 1982, 18, 41-

46; Bohlen, et al., Development of a woman's multiple orgasm
pattern: A research case report, JSR, 1982, 18, 130-145;
Waterman & Chiauzzi, The role of orgasm in male and female
sexual enjoyment, JSR, 1982, 18, 146-149; Bohlen, Female
ejaculation and urinary stress incontinence, JSR, 1982, 18,
360-363; Abramson & Pearsall, Pectoral changes during the
sexual response cycle: A thermographic analysis, ASB, 1983,
12, 357-368; Fisher et al., Patterns of female sexual arousal
during sleep and waking: Vaginal thermo-conductance studies,
ASB, 1983, 12, 97-122.

CHAPTER 9: SEXUAL DYSFUNCTION AND THERAPY

Topics Covered in Chapter

I. Sexual dysfunctions, organic factors with box on Kaplan's
categories of disorders and diseases that are associated with
sexual dysfunction, psychological factors including childhood
or adolescent trauma or misinformation, box on absence of sexual response during adulthood following incestuous childhood
experience, immediate source of dysfunction including anxiety,
guilt, etc.

II. Types of sexual dysfunctions, box on psychosexual disorders from the DSM-III, excessive and inhibited sexual desire,
inhibited excitement, inhibited female and male orgasm, premature ejaculation, functional dyspareunia, vaginismus,
priapism.

III. Sex therapy, Masters & Johnson's approach, discussion
on success rate for sex therapy, Kaplan's approach, treatment
techniques including systematic desensitization, nondemand
pleasuring and sensate focus, masturbatory training, stop-
start technique, squeeze technique, employment of sexual
surrogates and associated controversies, the use of surgery,
hormones, and drugs, sex therapists' qualifications and
ethical issues.

Use of Class Time. Analogous to "medical students' disease,"
some students think they have some of these dysfunctions.
We generally begin discussion of the dysfunctions with a discussion of differences in the sexual socialization of males
and females, and suggest that many females in our culture
may have some unlearning to do before being able to respond
easily when they want to.

Students generally get quite involved in the issue of
surrogate sexual partners. You might check the legal status
of surrogates in your state and ask students their opinions
on employment of surrogates. The International Professional
Surrogates Association (IPSA) can provide you with literature

about ethical guidelines and activities of their members.

Recent Research. Obler, A comparison of a hypnoanalytic/
behavior modification technique and a cotherapist-type
treatment with primary orgasmic dysfunctional females, JSR,
1982, 18, 331-345; Van Wyk, Relationship of time spent on
masturbation assignments with orgasmic outcome in pre-
orgasmic women's groups, JSR, 1982, 18, 33-40; Hoch, A commentary on the role of female sexological examination and
the personnel who should perform it, JSR, 1982, 18, 58-63
(plus 3 articles following Hoch's on the same topic);
DeWolfe & Livingston, Sexual therapy for a woman with
cerebral palsy, JSR, 1982, 18, 253-263; Evans & Zilbergeld,
Evaluating sex therapy: A reply to Kolodony, JSR, 1983,
19, 302-306; Procci et al., Consecutive-night reliability
of portable nocturnal penile tumescence monitor, ASB, 1983,
12, 307-316; Leff & Israel, The relationship between mode
of female masturbation and achievement of orgasm in coitus,
ASB, 1983, 12, 227-236; Snyder & Berg, Determinants of
sexual dissatisfaction in sexually distressed couples, ASB,
1983, 12, 237-246; Mitchell & Popkin, The pathophysiology
of sexual dysfunction associated with antipsychotic drug
therapy in males: A review, ASB, 1983, 12, 173-183;
Bancroft & Wu, Changes in erectile responsiveness during
androgen replacement therapy, ASB, 1983, 12, 59-66.

CHAPTER 10:   CONCEPTION AND PREGNANCY

Topics Covered in Chapter

I. Conception, increasing the chances of conceiving the
role of female arousal, gender selection techniques and moral
issues.

II. Infertility, box on emotional reactions, sources and
treatment of infertility in females, males, and couples, box
on in vitro fertilization, artificial insemination, surrogate
motherhood, adoption.

III. Pregnancy, early symptoms, false pregnancy, threats
to fetal development, description of characteristics of first,
second, and third trimester, debate over safety of sex late
in pregnancy, ectopic pregnancy, spontaneous abortion,
toxemia.

Use of Class Time. We treat chapters 10 and 11 as a unit,
so some of the suggestions for this chapter would also be
applicable for the next chapter. Your local hospital can

probably provide you with the names of some prepared childbirth
instructors who would be willing to give a lecture on the
basis of the techniques they use with couples during pregnancy
to prepare them for labor.

Recent issues of The New England Journal of Medicine and the
Journal of the American Medical Association can be consulted for
reports of the latest research on improving chances of conception, treatment of infertility, in vitro fertilization, fetal
surgery, treatment of pregnancy problems, and the issue of the
safety of sexual intercourse late in pregnancy. We report
Naeye's findings of greater incidence of amniotic fluid
infections in women having sex in the last few weeks of pregnancy,
but his conclusions have been contested and NEJM or JAMA may
have articles regarding this issue.

If it has not yet been shown, Miracle of Life would be appropriate while covering this chapter.

If you live near a local chapter of a surrogate motherhood
association (call your local medical society), you may be able
to get a surrogate mother as a guest speaker.

CHAPTER 11: BIRTH

Topics Covered in Chapter

I. Birth in other cultures and species, onset and location of
labor, first-stage labor, controversies over anesthesia, second
and third-stage labor, alternative approaches to labor and
birth including Lamaze and Leboyer methods and underwater birth.

II Childbirth complications, cesarean section, multiple births,
prematurity, low birth weight, postmaturity.

III. Postpartum events and decisions, comparison of breast
vs. bottle feeding, anatomy and physiology of breasts and lactation, circumcision controversies, postpartum adjustment,
sexual expression following birth.

Use of Class Time. The film, Birth of a Family, is extremely
well received by our students, second only to Miracle of Life
in their ratings, stimulating a lot of questions about the
birth process. Alternatively, if you have a Lamaze instructor
give a guest lecture, s/he may be able to provide the film
The Story of Eric.

We emphasize the importance of being knowledgeable about
labor and birth alternatives when hiring a physician to assist
in birth rather than trying to alter procedures after one is
in labor. One way to discuss of these controversies is to

47

find out the policies of your local hospitals and physicians regarding labor, the "prep," birthing rooms, rooming in, length of time following birth that a mother may nurse the infant, policies regarding midwives, willingness of local physicians to assist in a home delivery, etc. You could also see if there is a birthing center in your area, and request someone from the center to describe their procedures and policies, legal issues they face. Similarly, a member of an association of midwives may be able to provide a guest lecture.

CHAPTER 12: CONTRACEPTION

Topics Covered in Chapter

I. Development and use of modern contraceptives, political, social, technological, and medical issues, adolescent use (and nonuse) of contraceptives, contraceptive education, sexual attitudes and contraception, the male role, risks for women.

II. Methods of contraception including rhythm and the symptothermal method, diaphragm and spermicide, condom, contraceptive sponge, foams and suppositories, oral contraceptives, IUDs with box on Lippes' development of the loop, and relatively ineffective methods (withdrawal, postcoital douching, and breast-feeding).

III. Sterilization, vasectomy, tubal ligation, contraceptive techniques of the future.

Use of Class Time. We bring contraceptives to class describing the advantages and disadvantages of each and passing them around the class. There is invariably a lot of laughter as many people pass on the condoms as quickly as possible. If you get an inserter with the IUD, you can explain how it is inserted. You can probably obtain a set of contraceptives from Planned Parenthood or from a local pharmacist if you don't already have them. Students generally have a number of questions, and we think that the opportunity to handle the various contraceptives is superior to viewing them in a film.

Planned Parenthood is usually willing to provide a speaker to describe their services and the various methods.

Recent Research. See Herold & McNamee, An explanatory model of contraceptive use among young single women, JSR, 1982, 18, 289-304; Strahle, A model of premarital coital and contraceptive behavior among female adolescents, ASB, 1983, 12, 67-94; See Teenage Pregnancy: The problem that hasn't gone away: Alan Guttmacher Inst. N.Y. AGI, 1981. $4.50. Although we have

incorporated many of their findings in the book, this is
full of excellent graphs from which you can make transparencies.

CHAPTER 13: RESOLVING UNWANTED PREGNANCY

Topics Covered in Chapter

I. Legal status of abortion in the U.S., Supreme court
decisions of 1973 and 1983, the Hyde Amendment, the moral
debate over abortion with box on abortion vignettes used
in research on public policy decisions.

II. The abortion process, early methods, first trimester
methods with box describing the steps involved in suction
abortion, second-trimester methods with box describing the
use of prostaglandins, psychological responses to abortion
with box describing one woman's experience, male role in
abortion with box describing the debate over women's vs.
men's rights in abortion decisions.

III. Unplanned parenthood, single motherhood, single fatherhood, unwanted pregnancy, ethics, and advocacy of contraceptive education.

Use of Class Time. A debate between representatives of pro-
choice and pro-life groups is effective here. Our local
Planned Parenthood has a "panel of parents" that includes
single mothers, parents of single mothers, and sometimes,
single fathers who discuss their feelings about their decisions, what they would do differently if they had the
chance, etc. This is extremely well received by students,
and you might check to see if your PP or family planning
clinic has a similar program.

Recent issues of Family Planning Perspectives can be consulted
for the latest demographic data and legal status of abortion.

CHAPTER 14: SEXUALITY EARLY IN THE LIFE SPAN

Topics Covered in Chapter

I. Barriers to research on infant and childhood sexuality,
Freudian vs. Eriksonian models of psychosexual development.

II. Infancy, mother-child and father-child attachment, bio-
sexual and sensual development, parental reactions to infant
sensuality.

III. Toddlerhood, gender differences in labels children receive for their own sexual anatomy, toilet training and gender
differences in sexual associations, onset of awareness of
gender differences.

IV. Early childhood, sexual learning, the "primal scene"--
traumatic or educational, with suggestions for parental
handling of interruptions of children during lovemaking, box
on Mary Calderone's sex education, the Goldmans' study of
children's sexual knowledge, issues regarding the morality
of such research, the effect of physical attractiveness.

V. Late childhood, sex play, "doctor," etc., as sexual
rehearsal, box on B. F. Skinner's early experiences with
sexuality, homosocial bonds, box labeled sex education that
describes sex play with same gender people written by several
of our students as source of information about sexuality,
review of societal attitudes and practices toward sex education, desire of kids to get information from parents, but
getting information primarily from peers, etc., box on use
of "dirty words" for shock value, difficulties of obtaining
accurate information during childhood.

Use of Class Time. Storms' theory of the development of sexual preference can appropriately be introduced here. His
articles are referenced in the book, and we describe his theory
in Ch. 17 (Sexual Preference) but because of its complex
consideration of biological, psychological, and social factors,
it is helpful to students to describe it in lecture. If you
administered the questionnaire on p. 30 then you can provide
data from your students relevant to testing his theory.
If not, you might ask students to write down anonymously
their age in years and months at (a) menarche or first
nocturnal emission; (b) first masturbation; (c) first awareness of feelings they would now label as sexual arousal;
(d) first erotic fantasies of another person; (e) sexual
preference using Kinsey's 0-6 scale both in terms of behavior
and of fantasies.

A parent-child role play on sex discussions is both educational and fun for this chapter. If you have a small section,
the whole class can participate. For large sections, you can
request several volunteers. Ask the group to form dyads in
which one person is a parent and the other is a child. The
"child" asks questions that he asked (or wanted to ask) during
childhood. The parent responds first as his or her own parent
responded (or would have responded) and second as s/he plans
to respond if s/he becomes a parent. If and when students
become "stuck," you can tell them how Calderone & Ramey responded to various questions (see their book "Talking with Your
Child About Sex," NY: Random House, 1982). Calderone's book

50

with Eric Johnson, "The Family Book About Sexuality," is also helpful (NY: Harper & Row, 1981, or paper, NY: Bantam Books, 1983).

Recent Research. Simkins & Rinck, Male and female sexual vocabulary in different interpersonal contexts, JSR, 1982, 18, 160-172; Goldman & Goldman, Children's perceptions of sex differences in babies and adolescents: A cross-national study, ASB, 1983, 12, 277-294.

CHAPTER 15: ADOLESCENCE AND YOUNG ADULTHOOD

Topics Covered in Chapter

I. Adolescence and sexual and reproductive maturation in males and females, hypotheses about menstruation, box on menstruation and toxic shock syndrome, box with subjective descriptions of menarche, sexual exploration, the relationship between sexual and emotional intimacy, box on the role of sex in nonmarital adolescent relationships.

II. Young adulthood, lifestyle choices and shifting norms, single lifestyles, cohabitation, relationship contracts, box on questions for couples planning to cohabit, love and marriage, parenthood, division of labor, sexual expression.

Use of Class Time. Before students have read this chapter, you may want to outline, briefly, the comparisons made between conservative, moderate, and liberal couples in the Boston couples study described in the book, and ask students their hypotheses as to which group would be most likely to break up, and why they think so.

A panel of couples who vary from traditional (man involved in paid work, woman involved in family work) to modern (dual career) is very interesting to students. We have tried unsuccessfully to find couples who both have jobs (vs. careers) but they generally have less flexibility and can't take time off to come to a class. Students can be asked for written questions the day before the panel.

The film Achieving Sexual Maturity, though a little dated, is good at showing reproductive and sexual maturation with graphs and live nude models. You may want to discuss the masturbation sequence in class, as that portion of the film generally makes students a bit uncomfortable.

Recent Research. Zeiss, Expectations for the effects of aging on sexuality in parents and average married couples, JSR, 1982, 18, 47-57; Weis, Affective reactions to women to their initial experience of coitus, JSR; 1983, 19, 209-237;

Hatfield et al., Equity and sexual satisfaction in recently
married couples, JSR, 1982, 18, 18-32.

CHAPTER 16:   ADULTHOOD AND AGING

Topics Covered in Chapter

I. Sexuality and aging, the double standard of aging and the
media, adult sexual expression, long-term relationships,
extramarital sex and reasons for it, box with Lonny Myers
advocacy of open relationships, consensual extramarital sex,
box on group marriage, prostitution and legal status, box on
definitions of prostitution, box on massage parlors, separation and divorce, gender differences in adustment to separation.

II. Midlife changes and assessments, the climacteric, midlife
challenges and gender roles.

III. Old age, physiological changes in male and female sexual
systems, social stereotypes and self-image, aging and sexual
expression in both genders, decreasing sexual activity--aging
or other factors?, sexuality, aging, and health.

Use of Class Time. Several different panels are interesting
to students here. Several people in their fifties or older
who are willing to talk about their sexual feelings and expression and respond to student questions can be invited to
class. Alternatively, several couples involved in open and/or
group marriages can describe the pleasures and problems
associated with their life styles. A third possibility is
to invite a group of prostitutes to describe how they got
into the business and the advantages and disadvantages of
their jobs. Finally, members of Parents without Partners
can be invited to talk about the effect that being a single
parent has on their life and on their education of their
children for sexuality.

The movie A Ripple in Time can be shown although students
report exhausion at the vigor at which the older couple
makes love!

Recent Research. See Thompson, A. P. Review of the literature on extramarital sex, JSR, 1983, 19, 1-22; Spanier &
Margolis, Marital separation and extramarital sexual behavior,
JSR, 1983, 19, 23-48; Wheeler & Kilmann, Comarital sexual
behavior: Individual and relationship variables, ASB, 1983,
12, 295-306; Schenk, et al., Personality traits versus the
quality of the marital relationship as the determinant of
marital sexuality, ASB, 1983, 12, 31-42.

CHAPTER 17:   SEXUAL PREFERENCE

Topics Covered in Chapter

I. Definitions of sexual preferences, box on variations in
sexual preference and gender identities, cross-species and
cross-cultural comparisons, box on ethnocentric interpretations, legal and social status of homosexuality, criminal law,
box on immigration and sexual preference, gay liberation movement.

II. Homosexual behavior and gay identity, self-definition,
gay lifestyles, sexual expression, gender differences, aging,
situational homosexual expression.

III. Explanations of sexual preference, heredity, hormones,
childhood influences, Storms' theory of sexual preference.

IV. Sexual preference, adustment, and homophobia, box satiriz-
ing heterosexual (not homo.) pathology, therapy to change
preference, homophobia, box on Max Rafferty's refusal to give
gays teaching credentials.

V. Bisexuality, incidence, lifestyles.

Use of Class Time. As we noted earlier, Storms' theory tends
to be difficult for students to understand so if it hasn't
been discussed earlier, a description of it during lecture
can be helpful. If the questionnaire at the beginning of
this part was administered, data on the students are available
to see if the etiology of students' preferences are supportive
of Storms' theory.

A description of the theories tested by Bell, Weinberg, &
Hammersmith's book, Sexual Preference, Bloomington, IN: U.
of Indiana Press, 1981, is mentioned briefly in the text, but
can provide the basis of a good lecture. The book is highly
readable, although the biological inferences made in the concluding chapter are not based on any data collected by the
authors.

We generally devote two class sessions to this topic. We
discuss the various theories, concluding with a description
of Storms' theory in the first session. In the second, we
have a sexual preference panel that students really enjoy.
This panel is fairly large (8 to 10 people) and includes people
having hetero-, bi-, and homosexual preferences. You can
obtain volunteers for this panel if your campus has a gay
student union. Alternatively, a visit to a gay bar may yield
some people willing to volunteer. Although we have also used
a single gay speaker, we think the panel is preferable as
it is more likely to show the diversity in personality types,

gender role identification, etc. that exists in the gay community as well as among straights. We administer a short attitude survey before and after the panel's appearance. In the before form, we simply distribute a 7-point scale anchored at one end with "strongly approve of homosexuality" and at the other with "strongly disapprove of homosexuality" and asking for comments and the respondents' gender. In the after form, we distribute the same scale, and ask what the students liked and disliked about the panel. Although students' ratings always become more positive or accepting of homosexuality, one of the most frequent comments concerns the relationship between preference and physical attractiveness. That is, when a gay member of the panel is perceived as relatively attractive, students indicate surprise that the person is gay; alternatively, the perception of a gay as relatively unattractive leads to the attribution that the person can't attract members of the other gender. We discuss this at the beginning of the class session following the appearance of the panel.

Recent Research. Coleman et al., Arousability and sexual satisfaction in lesbian and heterosexual women, JSR, 1983, 19, 58-73; MacDonald, A. P., A little bit of lavendar goes a long way: A critique of research on sexual orientation, JSR, 1983, 19, 94-100; Ross, M. W., Societal relationships and gender role in homosexuals: A cross-cultural comparison, JSR, 1983, 19, 273-288; Bixler, R. H. Homosexual twin incest avoidance, JSR, 1983, 19, 296-302; McConaghy & Armstrong, Sexual orientation and consistency of sexual identity, ASB, 1983, 12, 317-327; Zuckerman & Myers, Sensation seeking in homosexual and heterosexual males, ASB, 1983, 12, 347-356; Whitman, Culturally invariable properties of male homosexuality: Tentative conclusions from cross-cultural research, ASB, 1983, 12, 207-226; Harry, Defeminization and adult psychological well-being among male homosexuals, ASB, 1983, 12, 1-19; Lieh-Mak et al., Lesbianism in the Chinese of Hong King, ASB, 1983, 12, 21-30; Dannecker's Theories of Homosexuality, London: Gay Men's Press, 1981, 123 pgs, $3.95, for a cross cultural review of explanations of same gender preference.

CHAPTER 18: DISEASES AND DISABILITIES

Topics Covered in Chapter

I. The social psychology of the STD epidemic, STDS and sexual attitudes.

II. STDs and genital infections; bacterial infections, including gonorrhea, NGU, syphilis, chanchroid, granuloma
inguinale, lymphogranuloma venereum (LGV), shigellosis; viral
infections including herpes-II, genital warts, hepatitis B;
vaginal infections including trichomoniasis, candidiasis,
hemophilus vaginalis; urinary tract and prostate infections
including cystitis and prostatitis; and parasitic infections
including amebiasis, enterobiasis, scabies, pediculosis pubis
(crabs); methods for reducing the risks of contracting STDs.

III. Cancer and sexuality, breast cancer, box on sex after
mastectomy, detection and diagnosis, treatment, breast reconstruction; cervical cancer, discussion of biological and
social-psychological factors involved in sexual response
after hysterectomy; cancers of the endometrium, prostate,
and testicles; acquired immune deficiency syndrome (AIDS).

IV. Diseases, handicaps, and sexual expression, cardiovascular illness, diabetes, spinal cord injuries, mental
retardation.

Use of Class Time. You may want to write to the Centers for
Disease Control requesting that you be put on their mailing
list for the latest information about STDs and AIDS. They
are in Atlanta, GA. We stress recognition of symptoms in
lecture (and in testing), and we spend most of our lecture
time on a description of the importance of notifying partners
and on the latest findings regarding gonorrhea, NGU, herpes,
and AIDS.

The film, Like Other People, is extremely good. You might
invite an administrator of a local institution for retarded
people to visit the class and answer students' questions
about institutional policies after seeing the movie. Alternatively, you may want to save this movie for Ch. 21, as it
has a lot to say about love.

CHAPTER 19: COERCIVE SEXUAL BEHAVIOR

Topics Covered in Chapter

I. Sexual assault, rape myths, box on sexual assault
stereotypes, victims, variations in sexual assault, male
assault victims, box on rape of males; offenders, early
experiences, sexual characteristics; explanations of assault,
victim precipitation, uncontrolled lust or uncontrolled
aggression?, exaggerated gender-role identity, violent pornography; the aftermath of sexual assault, box analogizing
mugging of a male to assault, rape crisis centers, reporting
assault to police, legal issues, changes in evidence
regarding consent.

II. Sexual harassment, research of early findings in employment settings, harassment in educational settings.

III. Sexual coercion of children, pedophilia, consequences
for the child; incest, box on cross-cultural norms, characteristics of offenders, consequences of incestuous relationships.

Use of Class Time. These last three chapters move along a
dimension from coercive to consensual relationships with
respect to power relationships. We lean heavily on the contribution of traditional gender role expectations to mis-
communication between males and females in the acquaintance
assault situation, and modeling appropriate assertiveness
in communication of feelings for both males and females
(making a distinction between assertion versus the expectation that females are to be coyly passive and males are to
demonstrate their masculinity by being sexually aggressive).
After this, however, it is important to note that the situation in some acquaintance assaults, stranger assault, some
kinds of harassment, and sexual relations with related or
unrelated children, aren't so likely to be solved with good
communication, since the offender is making use of power
(physical, psychological, economic, evaluative, age-related,
etc.) that is not available to the victim. Because childhood and adolescent sexual experiences are very common in
our culture, we generally return to the issue of "informed
consent" from Ch. 3 as a method of discussing issues of
guilt and responsibility for child-adult sexual interactions.

Members of pedophiliac or incest support groups can be
invited to form a panel describing their feelings about
their sexual experiences during childhood. Counselors
at a rape crisis may be invited to describe the procedures
they follow with their clients. A lawyer who handles assault
cases can be invited to speak on the laws in your state regarding marital assault, statutory rape, and age of consent,
etc.

Recent Research. Ellis & Beattie, The feminist explanation
for rape: An empirical test, JSR, 1983, 74-93; Korman &
Leslie, The relationship of feminist ideology and date expense sharing to perceptions of sexual aggression in dating,
JSR, 1982, 18, 114-129; Sarrel & Masters, Sexual molestation
of men by women, ASB, 1982, 11, 117-131; Rowland et al.,
Flirting between college students and faculty; JSR, 1982,
18, 346-359; Faley, Sexual harassment: Critical review of
legal cases with general principles and preventative measures,
Personnel Psychology, 1982, 35, 583-600.

CHAPTER 20: ATYPICAL SEXUAL ACTIVITY

Topics Covered in Chapter

I.   Paraphilias, box on DSM-III definitions of selected paraphilias, fetishes, exhibitionism, characteristics of exhibitionists, streaking and mooning, obscene phone calls, voyeurism, zoophilia, incidence and characteristics, sexual sadism and sexual masochism and beliefs about gender differences, box on the Marquis de Sade, necrophilia and other miscellaneous "philias."

II.   Treatment of paraphilias, psychotherapy, surgical castration, chemical treatment, aversion therapies, other approaches.

Use of Class Time.   A review of the conditioning process covered in Ch. 2 may be useful in reminding students that each of us develops conditioned responses to specific stimuli that may leave others' quite unaffected.   Continuing the theme begun in discussion of Ch. 18, we suggest that the fact that someone is turned on to something that most people think is strange isn't necessarily a problem.   It becomes problematic when someone else's rights to privacy are invaded, as with voyeurism, etc.

In addition to discussing appropriate responses to behavior of, say, an exhibitionist (suggestions that a number of our students have returned to tell us came in handy as they wandered around campus!), more coverage could be provided of attempts to treat paraphiliac behavior (see Kilmann ref. below).   The use of depo-provera, for instance, which is still quite new and controversial might be updated with any recent information on long term effects.

Recent Research.   Kilmann et al., The treatment of sexual paraphilias: A review of the outcome research, JSR, 1982, 18, 193-252; Kolarsky & Madlafousek, The inverse role of preparatory erotic stimulation in exhibitionists; Phallometric studies, ASB, 1983, 12, 123-148; Buhrich, The association of erotic piercing with homosexuality, sadomasochism, bondage, fetishism, and taboos, ASB, 1983, 12, 167-171.

CHAPTER 21: LOVING SEXUAL INTERACTIONS

Topics Covered in Chapter

I. Being loved, early experience, the primate studies, observations of neglected or abused children, cross-cultural observations.

II. Self-love vs. selfishness.

III. Loving others; forms of love including childhood love, friendship, erotic love, parental love, and humane love; falling in love, infatuation and physiological arousal, limerence, measuring love; lust vs. lust, feelings vs. behaviors, confusing lust, infatuation, and love.

IV. Love as dependency, jealousy, and other unlovely feelings; cases of mistaken identity?, box on love junkies, box on love as addiction, box on intimate terrorism (fears of abandonment vs. fears of engulfment).

V. Loving sexual interactions, vitality in long-term relationships.

Use of Class Time. Although most sex texts discussing love tend to use the terms agape, philia, eros, etc., we chose to discuss the development of the capacity to care about others using a life span perspective, but our "forms of love" can readily be related to these historical terms. We make a strong distinction between dependency and love, and suggest that among adults, unequal relations diminish the pleasure for both partners. We also discuss "lust" as legitimate feelings, but like all other feelings, one needs to make decisions about the ramifications of acting on various feelings. In discussing feelings of jealousy, dependency, etc., we emphasize the importance of recognizing the source of the feeling (oneself), owning the feeling with one's partner, and then describing the behavior of the other associated with the feeling rather than making attributions about the partner's motivations.

In use of class time for Ch. 16, we suggested inviting a panel of older people to discuss their sexual feelings and activities; for this topic, a panel of older couples could be invited to discuss their attraction/attachment feelings.

PART 3 TEST QUESTIONS

CHAPTER 1

PERCEPTIONS OF SEXUALITY: HISTORICAL AND CROSS-CULTURAL OVERVIEW

MULTIPLE-CHOICE QUESTIONS

    An asterisk to the left of the item indicates the correct answer.

1. In which of the following cultures was pederasty fairly common?
    (p. 14)   a. Egyptian   *b. Greek   c. Roman
    d. Mesopotamian

2. Which of the following cultures tolerated sexual activities
    for purposes other than reproduction? (p. 12)
    a. Hebrew   b. Christian   c. Mesopotamian   *d. Egyptian

3. The idea that not only overt actions but that also overt
    thoughts must be pure was originally stated by (p. 16)
    a. St. Augustine   *b. Jesus   c. St. Paul
    d. St. Thomas Acquinas

4. Many words now used to denote various sexual activities
    (e.g., fellatio, cunnilingus, and fornication) derive from
    the_____culture. (p. 15)
    *a. Roman   b. Greek   c. Hebrew   d. Egyptian

5. The most likely reason why circumcision was practiced in
    ancient Egypt was (p. 8)
    a. it was believed that circumcision reduced sexual desire
    in men and women   b. it was believed that circumcision
    prevented infection of the genitals   *c. circumcision
    was a ceremony signifying passage into sexual maturity and
    adulthood   d. none of the above

6. The term assexual means (p. 11)
    *a. having no sexual feelings   b. biologically part male
    and part female   c. sexual attraction to another person
    of the same gender   d. inability to reproduce

7. The form of marriage in which one man is married to two or
    more women is called (p. 8)
    a. monogamy   b. group marriage   c. polyandry   *d. polygyny

8. Which form of marriage is associated with agricultural economics? (p. 8)
    a. monogamy   c. group marriage   c. polyandry   *d. polygyny

9. Which of the following sequences is the one produced by Bachofen and Engels in their theory about matriarchal societies? (pp. 10-11)
    a. promiscuity, patriarchy, group marriage, matriarchy
    b. matriarchy, group marriage, promiscuity, patriarchy
    *c. promiscuity, group marriage, matriarchy, patriarchy
    d. matriarchy, patriarchy, group marriage, promiscuity

10. Early records of sexuality may be misleading because (pp. 6-7)
    a. the records reflect the views of only a select group of individuals   b. records may be distorted by ruling authorities   c. there is a tendency to read one's own thoughts and values into history   d. a and b
    *e. all of the above

11. The authors of the text believe (p. 5)
    a. we should ignore our own values and biases when making decisions concerning sexuality   *b. we should examine the accuracy of the assumptions underlying our values
    c. we should ignore other's values and rely on our own
    d. none of the above

12. Gagnon's major point is (p. 7)
    a. historical information about sexuality is often inaccurate
    b. those who ignore history about sexuality are doomed to repeat it   *c. there is a tendency to read into history our own thoughts and values   d. all of the above

13. In patriarchal societies (p. 11)
    a. offspring are given the father's name   b. offspring inherit from the father   c. a male god is worshipped
    *d. a and b   e. all of the above

14. Fornication is (p. 15)
    a. sexual intercourse using birth control   b. sexual intercourse between an adult and a child   *c. sexual intercourse between people who are not married to each other
    d. sexual intercourse for purposes other than procreation

15. The earliest records of sexuality come from (p. 6)
    a. the common people of the time   b. witch doctors
    c. scientists   *d. doctors and poets

16. According to Alan Watts, the characteristic pattern of modern American relationships is (p. 8)
    a. monogamy   *b. monogamy with partners continually being replaced   c. single life - no pairing of men and women
    d. polygamy

17. Which of the following types of relationships has been most infrequent? (p. 8)
    a. monogamy   b. homosexuality   *c. polyandry   d. polygyny

18. Females had somewhat higher status in_____culture. (pp. 11-12)
    a. Mesopotamian   *b. Egyptian   c. Hebrew   d. Roman

19. Prostitution first emerged in (p. 13)
    a. Christian culture   b. Hebrew culture
     c. the early Roman empire   *d. none of the above

20. According to St. Thomas Aquinas, which of the following were sins? (p. 20)
    a. coitus in unnatural positions   b. masturbation
    c. homosexuality   d. both a and b   *e. all of the above

21. Which of the following Christian writers supported sexual activities for purposes other than procreation? (pp. 17-20)
    a. St. Augustine   b. St. Thomas Aquinas   c. St. Paul
    *d. none of the above

22. Bachofen and Engel's theory about matriarchal societies has been questioned because   (p. 11)
    a. no patriarchal society has ever been discovered in the world   *b. no matriarchal society has ever been discovered in the world   c. there is no evidence that people ever worshipped fertility goddesses
    d. all of the above

23. Unlike Mesopotamia, a popular coital position during part of Egypt's history was (p. 12)
    a. man-above, woman-below   *b. woman-above, man-below
    c. rear entry   d. face to face, side by side

24. Rape was essentially theft in the_____culture. (p. 13)
    a. Greek   *b. Hebrew   c. Roman   d. Mesopotamian

25. In which of the following cultures was female homosexuality tolerated assuming it did not threaten the family? (pp. 11-14)
    a. Egyptian   b. Hebrew   c. Greek   d. a and c
    *e. all of the above

26. Which of the following cultures was tolerant of male homosexuality assuming it did not threaten the family? (p. 12, p. 14)
    a. Egyptian   b. Hebrew   c. Greek   *d. a and c
    e. all of the above

27. Which of the following cultures idealized male beauty? (p. 14)
    a. Egyptian   b. Hebrew   *c. Greek   d. Roman

28. In Roman culture education of the children was primarily the responsibility of (p. 15)
    *a. the mother   b. the father   c. siblings   d. a and b

29. Acts or feelings that Jesus condemned included (p. 16)
    *a. lust   b. sex   c. marriage   d. a and b
    e. all of the above

30. According to John Boswell, (p. 17)
    a. Christian theology was consistently opposed to homosexuality   b. Christian theology caused intolerance of homosexuality   *c. Christian theology was employed to justify oppression that had nonreligious motivation
    d. both a and c   e. all of the above

31. _____stated that a man is looking at his wife with lust is committing adultry. (p. 16, p. 18)
    a. Jesus   b. Pope John Paul II   c. St. Jerome
    *d. all of the above

32. Persecution of witches resulted primarily for_____
    reasons. (p. 21)
    a. religious   b. economical   c. political   *d. all of the above

33. Courtly love could be characterized by (p. 22)
    a. joining of hearts consumated by sexual intercourse
    b. a relationship that could occur only among married couples since sexual activity among unmarried couples was forbidden
    *c. a relationship that could occur only among the young since passion was too overwhelming for the elderly   d. all of the above

34. Which of the following statements concerning marriage is correct? (p. 23)
    a. early church leaders discouraged marriage at very young ages since youth was considered a period in which desire must be repressed   *b. Luther and Calvin both advocated marriage for the clergy   c. the Church has always been actively involved in uniting bride and groom
    d. in the 17th, 18th, and 19th centuries, church leaders supported marriage at a very young age to counteract uncontrolled lust

35. The Church tolerated prostitution during the early middle ages because (p. 23)
    a. laws banning prostitution were unenforceable
    b. no Christian doctrines condemned prostitution
    *c. the belief was that if there were no prostitutes, the world would be immersed in lust   d. none of the above; the Church did not tolerate prostitution at this time

36. Which of the following sexual activities was legal at the end of the 17th century in Europe? (p. 23)
    a. homosexuality   b. prostitution   c. adultery
    *d. none of the above

37. In 15th century France prostitution was widespread because (p. 24)
    a. it provided a large amount of funds for the towns
    b. it led to fewer rapes   *c. the married men had to compromise with unmarried men who were needed as a labor force
    d. the social order was declining

38. During which of the following eras were women considered as sexual temptresses luring men to sin? (p. 25)
    a. Mesopotamia   b. Middle Ages   c. Victorian era
    *d. both a and b   e. all of the above

39. A survey taken in the U.S. in the 1800's to indicate whether Victorian morality governed peoples' private lives revealed that   (p. 26)
    a. most women were reluctant to engage in sex
    b. few women used birth control   c. both a and b
    *d. neither a nor b

40. The leading figure in the pseudo-scientific linkage of nonreproductive sexual activity with disease was (pp. 27-28)
    *a. Krafft-Ebing   b. Ellis   c. Freud   d. all of the above

41. This individual attempted to broaden the spectrum of normal sexual behavior to include homosexuality and masturbation? (p. 28)
    a. Rush   b. Krafft-Ebing   *c. Ellis   d. none of the above

42. This scientist argued that in the process of becoming healthy adults, the source of pleasure and orgasm in women shifts from the clitoris to the vagina
    a. Rush   *b. Freud   c. Ellis   d. Krafft-Ebing

43. In which of the following cultures could women own property (p. 12)
    a. Mesopotamia   b. Hebrew   *c. Egyptian
    d. none of the above

TRUE-FALSE QUESTIONS

    A single underscore indicates the correct answer.

T F 1. In the Dark Ages sexual expression was a family matter and not of legal concern. (p. 19)

T F 2. Historically, most church leaders were quite tolerant of homosexuality and masturbation. (p. 17)

T <u>F</u> 3. Homosexuality has been quite widespread since the 14th century. (p. 20)

<u>T</u> F 4. Ellis argued that many sexual deviations were present at birth and represented only a variation from a statistical norm. (p. 28)

T <u>F</u> 5. Homosexuality was strongly disapproved of during the height of the Roman Empire. (p. 15)

<u>T</u> F 6. The Romans were more accepting of sexuality as part of their every day lives than the Greeks. (p. 15)

T <u>F</u> 7. The current day belief that love should precede marriage had its roots in Roman society. (p. 15)

<u>T</u> F 8. The belief that lust is a vice was a common theme in Christianity. (p. 18)

<u>T</u> F 9. Prostitution flourished in 15th-century France. (p. 24)

<u>T</u> F 10. Sexuality has been frequently perceived in conflict with spirituality. (p. 17)

<u>T</u> F 11. The belief that the purpose of sexual intimacy was procreation dominated most Western cultures. (p. 20)

T <u>F</u> 12. In most cultures and time periods women were perceived as passive and asexual beings. (p. 25)

T <u>F</u> 13. Intimate relationships between women have been punished more severely than intimate relationships between men. (p. 20)

T <u>F</u> 14. St. Thomas Aquinas lived during the Roman era. (p. 20)

T <u>F</u> 15. Contrary to religious authorities, scientists were much more tolerant of sexual practices such as homosexuality and masturbation. (pp. 26-27)

<u>T</u> F 16. In a survey by Mosher, it was found that many women defied the Victorian stereotype of the passionless female. (p. 26)

<u>T</u> F 17. Homosexuality was widespread in the 11th and 12th centuries in Europe. (p. 20)

<u>T</u> F 18. Both the Greeks and the Hebrews had very hostile attitudes toward sex. (pp. 12-15)

T <u>F</u> 19. Jesus gave extensive commentary on what sexual activities were permissable. (p. 16)

T F 20. In Greek society, the responsibility for education of the children was the duty of the father. (p. 14)

T F 21. The belief that fighting next to people toward whom there is sexual attraction reduces combat effectiveness derives from the Greek era. (p. 14)

T F 22. Attitudes among Hebrews toward women were more similar to those of the Mesopotamians than to those found in ancient Egypt. (p. 12)

T F 23. The worship of goddesses such as the Great Mother began in Greek and Roman civilization. (p. 10)

T F 24. Polygamy has been more prevalent in human cultures than has monogamy. (p. 8)

T F 25. Female circumcision has virtually disappeared from all cultures. (p. 7)

T F 26. The practice of performing genital surgery on both males and females probably began with the rise of Christianity. (p. 8)

CHAPTER 2

CONTEMPORARY EXPLANATIONS OF HUMAN SEXUALITY

MULTIPLE-CHOICE QUESTIONS

An asterisk to the left of the item indicates the correct answer.

1. In psychoanalytic theory, the level of personality corresponding to societal attitudes toward sexual behavior is (p. 43)
a. the libido   b. the id   c. the ego   *d. the superego

2. The defense mechanism which enables unacceptable sexual motives to be channeled into socially acceptable activities is called (p. 44)   *a. sublimation   b. reaction formation   c. projection   d. repression

3. The major purpose of scientific theory is to (p. 54)
a. alter personal or public policy decisions   *b. explain causes of behavior   c. change behavior   d. all of the above

4. In psychoanalytic theory, the ego attempts to compromise the demands of sexual instincts and societal sexual values using the (p. 43)
a. pleasure principle   *b. reality principle
c. perfection principle   d. none of the above

5. Early proponents of behaviorism maintained that sex researchers must focus on (p. 35)
a. sexual thoughts and desires   b. early childhood experiences   *c. observable sexual behavior   d. sexual interactions

6. Which of the following psychologists advanced the use of learning theory to study sexual response? (p. 35)
a. Freud   *b. Watson   c. Symons   d. Wilson

7. The Wild Boy of Aveyron was presented to highlight (pp.34-35)
a. sexual behavior in primitive societies   b. homosexuality   *c. sexual socialization   d. parental sexual abuse

8. Classical conditioning as a therapy for homosexuality (p.36)
*a. has generally been discontinued   b. has been quite successful   c. is a new technique that is just currently being investigated   d. has never been explored

9. Which of the following statements regarding the consequences of punishment is correct? (pp. 37-38)
a. in general punishment is not a very effective training strategy   b. the negative effects of punishment usually outweigh positive effects   c. punishment probably plays a role in the association of anxiety and guilt with sexual behavior   d. both b and c   *e. all of the above

10. Punishment is most effective in eliminating (pp. 37-38)
a. homosexuality   b. masturbation   c. pre-marital sex   *d. none of the above

11. A parent discontinues scolding a child after the child starts masturbating privately. This represents an application of the principle of (p. 36)
a. positive reinforcement   *b. negative reinforcement   c. punishment   d. extinction

12. A weakness of both instrumental and classical conditioning theories is that (p. 38)
a. they do not take the social context into account   b. they do not consider mental factors   c. they are difficult to test   *d. both a and b   e. all of the above

13. The individual most closely associated with social learning theory is (p. 38)
a. Watson   *b. Bandura   c. Freud   d. Symons

14. A factor that would be predicted to influence sexual behavior by social learning theorists but not by Freudian theorists or classical and instrumental conditioning theorists is (p. 38)
a. early childhood sexual experiences   b. one's religious orientation toward sexuality   c. whether a sexual attitude

or behavior has been directly reinforced   *d. whether one observes another's sexual attitudes or behaviors being reinforced

15. In which of the following theories is reinforcement important for acquiring sexual behaviors? (pp. 35-36, p. 38)
a. classical conditioning   b. instrumental conditioning
c. social learning theory   d. both a and b
*e. all of the above

16. The major purpose of symbolic interactionism is to   (p. 39)
a. explain how reinforcement influences sexual behavior
*b. explain the process of acquiring a sexual identity and the behaviors associated with that identity   c. explain how parents and children interact leading to the child acquiring sexual behaviors   d. explain how present day sexual behavior served the cause of reproductive success in the past

17. The concept of scripts is employed by   (p. 39)
a. evolutionary theorists   b. social learning theorists
c. Freudian theorists   *d. symbolic interactionists

18. Symbolic interactionism emphasizes   (p. 39)
a. fitness and inclusive fitness   b. hormonal and genetic influences   *c. labeling and roles   d. parent-child relationships

19. Which of the following conditions is necessary for scripted behavior to occur?   (p. 40)
a. a stable cognitive representation of the script
b. a context which leads the script to occur   c. a willing-ness to enter the script   *d. all of the above   e. none of the above

20. Freud's theory has been criticized because   (p. 47)
a. it is masculine in nature   b. it heavily emphasizes sexuality   c. it can not explain homosexual behavior
*d. both a and b   e. all of the above

21. In psychoanalytic theory, the sub-system of the mind that seeks only to gratify instinctual drives is   (p. 43)
*a. the id   b. the ego   c. the superego   d. the libido

22. In psychoanalytic theory, the attempt to satisfy instinctual drives by producing a mental image is called   (p. 43)
a. pleasure principle   b. reality principle
c. perfectionist principle   *d. wish-fulfillment

23. Freud placed great emphasis on the   (p. 43)
a. conscious   b. preconscious   *c. unconscious
d. all of the above

24. Censorship of sexual thoughts and behavior takes place at the
_____level. (p. 43)
a. conscious   *b. preconscious   c. unconscious
d. all of the above

25. Defense mechanisms are strategies used by the   (p. 43)
a. id   *b. ego   c. superego   d. all of the above

26. Defense mechanisms are alike in that they   (p. 44)
a. deny or distort reality   b. operate on an unconscious
level   c. disrupt effective personality functioning
d. both a and b   *e. all of the above

27. The Oedipal conflict first flares up during the_____
stage.   (p. 46)
a. oral   b. anal   *c. phallic   d. genital

28. Clashes of will between parents and child are characteristic
of the_____stage.   (p. 46)
a. oral   *b. anal   c. phallic   d. genital

29. Freud differed from more contemporary psychoanalytic theorists
in that   (p. 47)
a. he emphasized the genital stage   *b. his theories were
mainly masculine in nature   b. he emphasized interpersonal relations   d. both a and b   e. all of the above

30. Freud's major contribution was that   (p. 47)
a. he carried out many systematic experiments to test his
theory   b. he realized that orgasms result from
clitoral stimulation   *c. he recognized the importance
of early childhood experiences in the development of normal
and abnormal sexual behavior   d. he was able to explain
homosexual behavior using the Oedipal conflict

31. Erickson's theory is concerned mostly with_____factors.
(p. 48)
a. biological   b. psychological   c. environmental
d. both a and b   *e. all of the above

32. The sub-system of the mind emphasized by Freud was the (p. 43)
*a. id   b. ego   c. superego   d. all were emphasized
equally

33. Modern evolutionary theory is based on the work of   (p. 48)
a. Freud   b. Darwin   c. Mendel   d. both a and b
*e. both b and c

34. According to Strehler, the rapid changes in the evolutionary
process which produced our present species was due to   (p.50)
a. environmental or climate changes   *b. polygamy
c. altruistic behavior   d. all of the above

35. The principle discovered by Darwin which is used in evolu-
    tionary theories is (p. 48)
    a. fitness   b. inclusive fitness   *c. natural selection
    d. none of the above

36. How do evolutionary theorists explain observed gender differ-
    ences in courtship behavior? (p. 51)
    a. differences in the extent to which males and females are
    rewarded for taking the initiative   b. contemporary roles
    and scripts which label a sexually assertive man as healthy
    and a sexually assertive woman as "easy"   c. fundamental
    biological/psychological aspects of male and female sexuality
    *d. amount of investment in offspring made by males versus
    females

37. According to Trivers, in species where females invest more
    time and resources in offspring than males,
    *a. male-male competition for female mates will be greater
    than female-female competition for male mates
    b. there will be a greater range in reproductive success
    among females than males   c. there is greater selective
    pressure on females than males   d. a and b   e. all of
    the above

38. An evolutionary theorist's explanation of homosexuality would
    be (p. 53)
    a. over the years homosexual behavior has been rewarded and
    heterosexual behavior has been punished   b. a substantial
    proportion of people who engage in homosexual behavior are
    heterosexually married and have children   *c. inclusive
    fitness of homosexuals is increased by helping one's relatives
    with the same genes   d. evolutionary theory cannot ex-
    plain homosexual behavior

39. Which of the following theories is easiest to test experi-
    mentally? (p. 35)
    *a. learning theory   b. Freudian theory   c. evolutionary
    theory   d. all of these theories are easy to test

40. According to evolutionary theory, which of your grandparents
    should shower you with the most gifts; that is, which grand-
    parent has invested the most in your reproductive success
    (pp. 51-52)
    a. paternal grandfather   b. paternal grandmother
    c. maternal grandfather   *d. maternal grandmother

41. Evolutionary theory can be criticized because (p. 51)
    a. it states that human are forced by our "inherited"
    characteristics to behave in unavoidably determined ways
    b. it cannot explain behavior such as male assertiveness or
    homosexuality

*c. it is difficult to test   d. the theory advocates
practices such as genetic engineering

42. Freud would say that incest results from a failure to resolve
conflicts at the_____stage. (p. 46)
a. oral   b. anal   *c. phallic   d. genital

43. According to Freud, the young boy represses his sexual desire
for his mother because (p. 47)
a. his mother shows no interest   b. he is too young
c. he learns to prefer girls his own age   *d. he fears his
father will castrate him

44. Which of the following is an assumption in Wilson's sociobiological explanation of homosexuality? (p. 53)
a. there are genes for homosexual preference   b. organisms
attempt to enhance the reproductive success of their relatives
c. homosexuals don't reproduce   d. a and b
*e. all of the above

TRUE-FALSE QUESTIONS

A single underscore indicates the correct answer.

T F 1. Humans spend little time engaging in sexual or quasi-
sexual activities. (pp. 32-33)

T F 2. The major purpose of a theory is to advocate a particular viewpoint. (p. 33)

T F 3. Early behaviorists concerned themselves primarily with
overt sexual behavior and disregarded sexual thoughts,
ideas, beliefs, or attitudes. (p. 35)

T F 4. Freud used a behaviorist approach when studying
sexuality. (p. 41)

T F 5. A major weakness of classical and instrumental conditioning approaches to the study of sexual behavior is that
they fail to consider the social context. (p. 38)

T F 6. According to classical conditioning theory, sexual
behavior is influenced by what comes after it - its
consequences. (p. 35)

T F 7. Negative reinforcement is the application of an aversive
stimulus after an undesirable sexual behavior. (p. 36)

T F 8. Punishment may temporarily stop a sexual behavior, but
the behavior generally reappears out of sight of the
person who did the punishing. (p. 37)

70

T F 9. Social learning theorists emphasize mental events. (p. 38)

T F 10. Symbolic interactionists believe that sexual preference is a permanent trait that people have within themselves. (p. 39)

T F 11. From the standpoint of script theory, there is little sexual behavior that can truly be called spontaneous. (p. 40)

T F 12. Research has indicated that college students' views of sexual interactions are very scripted. (p. 40)

T F 13. Major differences have been found between male and female scripts of sexual interactions. (p. 40)

T F 14. Freud argued that the child was pure and asexual. (p. 41)

T F 15. Freud's theories strongly reflect the influence of the Victorian era. (p. 41)

T F 16. According to Freud, sexual energy, or libido, was the source of all human endeavors. (p. 41)

T F 17. Freud believed society socialized children's sexuality too severely. (p. 41)

T F 18. Projection is a defense mechanism in which we attribute to others our own unacceptable feelings or ideas. (p.44)

T F 19. The Oedipal conflict usually resurfaces during the latency stage. (p. 46)

T F 20. The Oedipal conflict is resolved by developing an identity with the parent of the same gender. (p. 46)

T F 21. Freud gathered most of the evidence of his theory from analysis of his patients and himself. (p. 45)

T F 22. Most refinements of psychoanalytic theory have stressed the importance of the superego. (p. 48)

T F 23. Erikson's theory of personality development is even more pessimistic than Freud's. (p. 48)

T F 24. According to Strehler, democratic mating patterns should slow down evolutionary change. (pp. 49-50)

T F 25. Sociobiologists are primarily concerned with proximate (contemporary) questions about how a particular behavior came to exist. (p. 51)

T F 26. Evidence indicates that both males and females report that males are more assertive than females in initiating sexual activity. (p. 51)

T F 27. According to Trivers, in species where males have greater parental investment, females will demonstrate greater competitiveness and sexual aggressiveness. (p. 52)

T F 28. According to sociobiologists, evidence supports the conclusion that promiscuity, active courtship, and belligerance toward rivals are inherent characteristics of maleness. (pp. 51-52)

T F 29. An evolutionary view of behavior implies that humans are forced to behave in unavoidably determined ways. (p.51)

CHAPTER 3

RESEARCH ON SEXUALITY

MULTIPLE-CHOICE QUESTIONS

An asterisk to the left of the item indictes the correct answer.

1. Which of the following is a nonscientific factor that influences sexuality research? (pp. 84-86)
a. availability of funds for research   b. societal complaints that such research is immoral   c. principle of informed consent   *d. all of the above

2. Which of the following is a scientific factor that influences sexuality research? (pp. 60-61)
a. availability of funds for research   b. ethical concerns
*c. generalizability of research findings   d. societal objections to research

3. One Congressman has criticized Senator Proxmire's attacks on research on love because (p. 86)
a. research is not as expensive as Senator Proxmire says
b. research on love is interesting   *c. research on love might ease the divorce problem   d. none of the above

4. Research using a new drug which might potentially be dangerous can be justified using (p. 85)
a. informed consent   *b. risk benefit principle
c. freedom from coercion   d. all of the above

5. The principle of informed consent involves (p. 61)
a. telling subjects about embarrassing or damaging aspects of

72

the research before they agree to participate
b. permitting the opportunity to refuse to participate
c. justifying research on the basis that the benefits outweigh the risks   *d. both a and b   e. all of the above

6. Which of the following is a testable hypothesis without
    further operational definitions. (p. 59)
    a. love is the answer to all sexual problems   *b. males
    and females differ in their self-reported sexual arousal to
    erotic films   c. abortion violates the rights of the
    unborn fetus   d. societal reactions make human sexuality
    research difficult to conduct

Questions 7, 8, and 9 should be answered after reading the following one sentence description of a research study. In a study designed to measure the effect of erotic material on sexual arousal
in males, the type of erotic material was varied.

7. The type of erotic material is (p. 59)
    *a. an independent variable   b. a dependent variable
    c. a control variable   d. none of the above

8. The sex of the subjects (males) is   (p. 60)
    a. an independent variable   b. a dependent variable
    *c. a control variable   d. none of the above

9. The amount of sexual arousal is (p. 60)
    a. an independent variable   *b. a dependent variable
    c. a control variable   d. none of the above

10. In an experimental study we measure the____variable after
    manipulating the____variable and holding____variables con-
    stant. (pp. 59-60)
    a. independent, dependent, control   b. control, independent,
    dependent   *c. dependent, independent, control
    d. control, dependent, independent

11. In which of the following word pairs do both words have the
    same meaning? (p. 60)
    a. stimulus - consequent event   b. stimulus - response
    c. response - antecedent event   *d. none of the above

12. Which of the following is important when testing a hypothesis?
    (p. 59)
    a. the experimenter should believe in the hypothesis
    b. the hypothesis must be one that has been supported many
    times in other research studies   *c. the variables must be
    defined in such a way that they can be measured or counted
    d. all of the above

13. In research it is <u>essential</u> that (p. 59)
    *a. variables be defined in such a way that people can agree
    on what is meant by the variables   b. all variables be
    controlled   c. research be first done in the laboratory
    and then in the field   d. non-reactive measures be used

14. Humphrey's research on homosexuality can be criticized on the
    grounds that (p. 84)
    *a. his study violated ethical principles   b. his
    hypotheses were not testable   c. his findings were not
    generalizable   d. he did not define his variables

15. In most research we (p. 62)
    a. take a population and generalize to the sample
    *b. take a sample and generalize to the population
    c. take a population and do not try to generalize
    d. take a sample and do not try to generalize

16. Since volunteer bias is a large problem in sexuality research
    (pp. 61-62)
    a. we should choose less biased subjects   b. the usefulness
    of sex research is quite limited   *c. we should be care-
    ful when generalizing results   d. we should try to get
    nonvolunteers to participate

17. Which of the following is true about volunteers in sexuality
    studies (p. 63)
    a. more than half are women .   *b. they have more noncoital
    sexual experience   c. they are more conservative
    d. they date less frequently

18. Sex research may obtain inaccurate reports from their
    respondents as a result of (p. 63)
    a. errors in memory   b. intentional and unintentional
    distortion of facts   c. subjects misunderstanding ques-
    tions   *d. all of the above

19. Masters and Johnson use direct observation to reduce the
    problem of (p. 64)
    *a. self-report bias   b. artificiality
    c. reactivity   d. volunteer bias

20. Assume that consumption of Vitamin E and sexual prowess are
    highly correlated. We can say that (p. 64)
    a. Vitamin E causes sexual prowess   b. sexual interest
    increases after consuming Vitamin E   c. either a is true
    or b is true   *d. none of the above

21. Variables other than independent variables that can influence
    the outcomes of experiments can be controlled by (p. 60)
    a. doing a correlational study   b. holding the variables
    constant   c. using randomization   *d. both a and c
    e. all of the above

22. A person scores 100 on a measure of sex guilt and a few months later scores 100 again on the same test. This indicates that the sex guilt test is (p. 72)
*a. reliable   b. valid   c. both reliable and valid
d. generalizable

23. It was observed in a study of thirty cities that increased availability of pornography was unrelated to assault. This is an example of (p. 64)
*a. a correlational study   b. a longitudinal study
c. a laboratory study   d. none of the above

24. An advantage of the correlational over the experimental method is that (p. 65)
a. one can determine cause and effect   b. one can control other variables   c. one can measure variables more accurately   *d. one can generalize results more readily

25. Allgeier's research on the So tribe is an example of (p. 69)
a. experimental research   *b. field research
c. laboratory research   d. both a and c

26. In Allgeier's research on the So tribe which of the following measures were used (p. 69)
a. physiological measures   b. self-administered questionnaires   *c. interviews   d. all of the above

27. An advantage of the experimental method over the correlational method is that (p. 66)
a. results are less reactive   b. results are less artificial
*c. one can infer cause and effect   d. none of the above

28. An advantage of interviews over questionnaires is that interviews are (p. 73)
a. cheaper   b. more anonymous   *c. more flexible
d. none of the above

29. An advantage of the direct observation method over all other methods is that (p. 74)
*a. it virtually eliminates the possibility of data falsification through memory deficits and distortions of facts
b. it is more accurate than other methods   c. it is less reactive than other methods   d. all of the above

30. Which of the following research methods would be appropriate to study the effects of different drugs on sexual response? (pp. 65-66)
*a. experimental research   b. questionnaires
c. case studies   d. interviews

31. Which of the following methods is least expensive? (p. 79)
*a. surveys   b. direct observation   c. interviews
d. physiological measures

32. Which of the following measures is most subjective? (p. 79)
    *a. paper and pencil tests   b. physiological measures
    c. direct observation   d. biological measures

33. Which of the following measures is least reactive? (p. 79)
    *a. surveys   b. interviews   c. physiological measures
    d. biochemical measures

34. If a sex guilt measure has high test-retest reliability (p. 72)
    a. people get about the same score on two similar forms of
    the test   *b. people get about the same score on the
    same sex guilt measure at two different testing periods
    c. people with similar attitudes get about the same score on
    the sex guilt measure   d. none of the above

35. Content validity of a sexual knowledge survey refers to (p.72)
    a. the effectiveness of the survey in predicting a person's
    arousal in specified situations   *b. whether the items
    in the survey really indicate the amount of sexual knowledge
    that people possess   c. the degree to which people get
    about the same score on two different versions of the survey
    d. the degree to which people get about the same score at two
    different times on the same guilt test

36. Which of the following methods represents the best way to
    test the hypothesis that there is a distinction between
    clitoral and vaginal orgasms? (p. 76)
    a. self-administered surveys   b. interviews
    c. direct observation   *d. physiological measures

37. The most frequently used measure of female genital response
    is a (p. 76)
    a. mercury-in-rubber strain gauge   b. metal-band gauge
    *c. photoplethysmograph   d. none of the above

38. Which of the following is an advantage of thermographic
    measures over biochemical measures? (p. 78)
    a. they are less intrusive   b. they are less reactive
    c. the same measures can be used for both men and women
    *d. all of the above

39. Which of the following are problems in the Hite Report on
    Sexuality? (pp. 62-63)
    a. volunteer bias   b. self-report bias   c. measurement
    problems   *d. all of the above

40. Which of the following methods was used by Kinsey to deter-
    mine the reliability of volunteer's responses? (pp. 73-74)
    a. volunteers were reinterviewed   b. husbands' and wives'
    responses on questions which should have the same answers
    were compared   c. different investigators were used
    to code responses   *d. all of the above

41. Byrne's study on computer dating used (p. 68)
    a. the experimental method   b. the correlational method
    c. both a and b   d. neither a nor b

42. Most of Byrne's research on attraction has (p. 68)
    *a. used the experimental method   b. used the correlational
    method   c. been field research   d. both b and c

43. Counterbalancing items on a scale helps to reduce what type
    of response bias (p. 73)
    a. responding in a way to please the experimenter
    b. responding only to certain items   *c. responding the
    same way on all items (e.g., agreeing or disagreeing on all
    items)   d. all of the above

44. Which of the following research studies used interviews as
    the major research method? (p. 73)
    a. Master's and Johnson's research on sexual responding
    *b. Kinsey et al.'s research on sexual attitudes
    c. Byrne's research on computer dating   d. Vassey's re-
    search on the relationship between Vitamin E and sexual
    prowess

45. Which of the following populations was underrepresented in
    the Kinsey studies? (p. 73)
    a. middle class   *b. ethnic minorities   c. well-educated
    d. both b and c

TRUE-FALSE QUESTIONS

    A single underscore indicates the correct answer.

T F 1. If a measure of sexual attitudes is reliable then it
          must be valid. (p. 72)

T F 2. Sex research has been primarily a twentieth century
          endeavor. (p. 86)

T F 3. Cross-sectional research involves comparisons of
          different groups over the same time period. (pp. 70-71)

T F 4. The correlational method is used to show cause and
          effect. (p. 64)

T F 5. Generally, most field studies use the experimental
          method. (p. 86)

T F 6. Volunteer bias is only a problem if there are system-
          atic differences between volunteers and non-volunteers
          on the variables being studied. (p. 61)

T <u>F</u> 7. Kinsey took large steps to insure that he obtained a sample representative of all social classes and all areas of the country. (p. 73)

T <u>F</u> 8. If research poses a potential psychological danger, then according to the ethical principle of freedom from coercion, the research can still be performed. (p. 84)

<u>T</u> F 9. Interviews allow for greater flexibility in acquiring information than surveys. (p. 73)

T <u>F</u> 10. Kinsey found accuracy of volunteer reports to be good regardless of whether the questions concerned demographics or frequency of marital intercourse. (p. 74)

T <u>F</u> 11. The major advantage of longitudinal research over cross-sectional research is that it is less time consuming and less expensive. (p. 71)

<u>T</u> F 12. Measures such as GSR and heart rate do not differentiate general arousal and sexual arousal. (p. 76)

T <u>F</u> 13. Radioimmunoassay and gas chromatographic methods involve analysis of urine for testosterone. (p. 78)

<u>T</u> F 14. A major advantage of direct observation over questionnaires is the reduction of self-report bias. (p. 64)

<u>T</u> F 15. Volunteer bias is a greater problem when using direct observation than when using questionnaires. (p. 75)

<u>T</u> F 16. Guaranteeing anonymity is one way of reducing self-report bias. (p. 75)

T <u>F</u> 17. An independent variable is held constant to reduce its effect on the dependent variable. (pp. 59-60)

T <u>F</u> 18. Descriptive statistics are used to determine if differences are statistically reliable. (p. 66)

T <u>F</u> 19. A p value of .80 in a study indicates that one has found a reliable difference. (p. 72)

<u>T</u> F 20. A placebo is a treatment which is effective because people believe it is effective rather than due to the properties of the treatment. (p. 82)

<u>T</u> F 21. Biochemical measures of sexual arousal are less reactive than physiological measures. (p. 78)

T <u>F</u> 22. The ability to do sex research has not been greatly affected by nonscientific factors. (pp. 84-86)

CHAPTER 4

SEXUAL ANATOMY AND PHYSIOLOGY

MULTIPLE-CHOICE QUESTIONS

An asterisk to the left of the item indicates the correct
answer.

1. Each of the testes is suspended at the end of (p. 90)
    a. an ejaculatory duct   b. the seminiferous tubules
    c. the vas deferens   *d. a spermatic cord

2. The_____encircles the testes and raises it closer to the
    body in response to cold, fear, anger, and sexual arousal.
    (p. 90)
    a. scrotum   *b. cremaster muscle   c. epididymis
    d. corpora cavernosa

3. Sperm are produced in the (p. 90)
    *a. seminiferous tubules   b. vas deferens
    c. spermatic cord   d. ejaculatory ducts

4. Semen is composed of (p. 91)
    a. fluid from the seminal vesicles   b. fluid from the
    prostate gland   c. sperm   d. both b and c
    *e. all of the above

5. The function of the urethra in the male (p. 91)
    a. conveys urine   b. conveys semen   c. stores sperm
    *d. both a and b   e. all of the above

6. The seminal vessicles are located (p. 92)
    a. directly beneath the glans   *b. on either side of
    the bladder   c. inside the scrotum at the base of the
    testes   d. on either side of the spermatic cord

7. The Cowper's glands secrete a fluid which (p. 92)
    a. regulates the temperature in the urethra   b. may in-
    crease the capacity of sperm to swim when deposited in the
    vagina   *c. may help neutralize the acidic effect of
    urine in the urethra   d. all of the above

8. On the average an erect penis is (p. 93)
    a. about one inch longer than a flaccid penis   *b. a little
    less than twice the size of a flaccid penis   c. a little
    more than twice the size of a flaccid penis   d. a little
    more than twice the diameter of a flaccid penis

9. Which of the following is part of the internal genitals of a
    male? (p. 92)
    a. scrotum   b. prepuce   *c. prostate   d. penis

10. The foreskin of the penis is also called (p. 93)
    a. corona   b. frenulum   c. glans   *d. prepuce

11. The penis is most sensitive (p. 93)
    a. all along the shaft   b. at the base near the scrotum
    *c. at the glans   d. at the prepuce

12. The rigidity of the penis when erect is due to (p. 93)
    a. tightening of the cremaster muscle   b. firmness of the
    urethra   *c. dilation of blood vessels which become
    filled with blood   d. none of the above

13. Penis size is most highly related to (p. 94)
    a. sexual prowess   b. height   c. both a and b
    *d. none of the above

14. Which of the following is part of the female anatomy? (p. 100)
    *a. Bartholin's glands   b. Cowper's glands
    c. epididymis   d. frenulum

15. The purpose of the epididymis is to (p. 90)
    a. transport sperm in the penis   *b. store sperm
    c. produce sperm   d. contribute fluid to semen

16. The Grafenberg spot is (p. 97)
    a. external   *b. located in the upper wall of the vagina
    c. sensitive to soft stroking   d. located only in cer-
    tain women

17. The ovaries are similar to the testes in that (pp. 94-95)
    a. they develop from the same tissue   b. they both produce
    reproductive cells   c. both secrete hormones
    *d. all of the above

18. The principal feminizing hormones are (p. 95)
    *a. estrogen and progesterone   b. estrogen and testosterone
    c. progesterone and androgen   d. testosterone and androgen

19. Fertilization usually occurs in the (p. 96)
    a. uterus   *b. fallopian tubes   c. space between the
    ovaries and the fallopian tubes   d. ovaries

20. The ovum is transported through the fallopian tubes by
    (p. 96)
    a. tiny muscles in the fallopian tubes   b. a fluid secreted
    by the fallopian tubes   *c. hairlike structures in the
    fallopian tubes   d. none of the above

21. The uterus is (p. 96)
    *a. suspended in the pelvic cavity by ligaments   b. composed
    of striated muscle   c. the organ that contains the
    Grafenberg spot   d. a thin-walled muscular tube

22. Which of the following statements about the Grafenberg spot is true? (p. 99)
a. most women are able to stimulate the spot themselves using their fingers   b. stimulation of the spot leads to ejaculation in most women   *c. Perry and Whipple have located the spot in every woman tested   d. the spot can usually be stimulated by intercourse in the missionary position (man above woman)

23. Stress incontenance refers to (p. 99)
*a. inability of females to prevent urination at orgasm
b. failure of women to achieve orgasm   c. anxiety pre-venting satisfaction during intercourse   d. none of the above

24. The external genitals of the female are known collectively as (p. 99)
a. labia majora   b. clitoris   c. mons pubis   *d. vulva

25. Which of the following parts in the female is most erotically sensitive (p. 101)
a. labia majora   *b. clitoria   c. vagina   d. mons pubis

26. The clitoris is similar to the penis in that (p. 101)
a. both are connected to the urethra   b. both contain the corpus spongiosum   *c. both develop from the same tissue during prenatal growth   d. none of the above

27. Which of the following statements about the hymen is true? (p. 101)
a. first intercourse for a woman is often painful because of rupture of the hymen   b. the presence of the hymen is usually a reliable indicator of virginity   c. its purpose is to partially block the entrance of the vagina so that menstrual fluid can be retained   *d. none of the above

28. The purpose of the Kegel exercises is to (p. 103)
a. reduce anxiety during sexual arousal   *b. improve genital muscle tone   c. to strengthen the uterine muscles in females which contract during childbirth
d. all of the above

29. Responsiveness to stimulation of the breasts is influenced most by (p. 105)
*a. learning   b. number of touch and pressure receptors
c. number of nerve endings   d. size of the breasts

30. The breasts are primarily composed of (p. 103)
a. smooth muscle   b. striated muscle
*c. fatty tissue   d. touch and pressure receptors

31. Which of the following is part of the male anatomy? (p. 91)
    a. Bartholin's glands   b. mons pubis   c. cervix
    *d. vas deferens

32. Ovaries in the female are to testes in the male as (p. 95,
    p. 101)
    a. ova are to sperm   b. Bartholin's glands are to Cowper's
    glands   c. clitoris is to penis   *d. all of the above

33. The womb is also called (p. 96)
    a. vulva   b. cervix   *c. uterus   d. vagina

34. Women may become impregnated from sperm in fluid from the
    _____prior to male ejaculation. (p. 92)
    *a. Cowper's glands   b. prostate gland   c. epididymis
    d. seminal vesicles

35. The primary function of the prostate gland is to (p. 92)
    a. store sperm   b. supply fluid to neutralize the acidity
    in the urethra   *c. supply much of the seminal fluid
    d. supply substances such as fructose that increase sperm
    motility

36. The_____nervous system prepares the body for emergencies.
    (p. 107)
    a. peripheral   b. central   *c. sympathetic
    d. parasympathetic

37. The autonomic nervous system lies within the (p. 106)
    a. central nervous system   *b. peripheral nervous system
    c. somatic nervous system   d. none of the above

38. The_____nervous system is involved in initial arousal and
    the_____nervous system is involved in orgasm. (p. 107)
    a. sympathetic; sympathetic   b. sympathetic; parasympathetic
    *c. parasympathetic; sympathetic   d. parasympathetic;
    parasympathetic

39. The phase in which semen is moved from the testicles through
    the vas deferens to the base of the penis is known as (p. 107)
    a. orgasm   *b. emission   c. ejaculation   d. expulsion

40. The_____nervous system is involved in emission and the
    _____nervous system is involved in expulsion. (p. 107)
    a. sympathetic; sympathetic *b. sympathetic; parasympathetic
    c. parasympathetic; sympathetic   d. parasympathetic; para-
    sympathetic

41. The two nerves that run between the genitals and the spinal
    cord that are important in the erotic response of males are
    (p. 109)
    *a. pudendal, pelvic   b. pelvic, penile   c. penile,
    pudendal   d. none of the above

42. The arousal center of the brain is the (p. 111)
    a. medulla   *b. reticular activating system
    c. thalamus   d. all of the above

43. Ejaculation centers are located in the (p. 110)
    *a. thalamus   b. reticular activating system
    c. medulla   d. all of the above

44. The hypothalamus is important in the control of (p. 110)
    a. reproductive cycles in the female   b. lactation in fe-
    males   c. production of masculinizing sex hormones in
    males and females   *d. all of the above

45. Pleasure centers are located in (pp. 111-112)
    a. thalamus   b. hypothalamus   c. limbic system
    *d. both b and c   e. all of the above

46. Which of the following structures belongs to the limbic
    system? (p. 112)
    a. thalamus   b. hypothalamus   c. pituitary gland
    *d. none of the above

47. Destruction of the temporal lobe in rhesus monkeys leads to
    (p. 112)
    a. failure to achieve orgasm   b. an increase in emotional
    and aggressive behavior   c. inappropriate mothering behav-
    ior   *d. bizarre sexual behavior

48. Smell is mediated by (p. 112)
    a. the thalamus   b. the hypothalamus   *c. limbic system
    d. temporal lobes

49. The major function of the cerebrum concerning sexual behavior
    is (p. 111)
    a. self-preservation   b. arousal   c. motivation and
    emotion   *d. control and integration of sexual behavior

50. Which of the following are endocrine glands? (p. 113)
    *a. testes   b. prostate gland   c. Cowper's glands
    d. Bartholin's glands

51. The_____lies on top of the kidneys. (p. 113)
    *a. adrenal glands   b. bladder   c. pituitary gland
    d. none of the above

52. Luteinizing hormone (LH) (p. 113)
    *a. stimulates ovulation   b. induces ovarian follicles to
    mature   c. stimulates sperm production in the testes
    d. stimulates lactation

53. Which of the following substances are secreted by the
    adrenal glands? (p. 113)   a. prolactin   *b. androgen
    c. oxytocin   d. follicle stimulating hormone (FSH)

54. Prolactin and oxytocin (p. 113)
    a. affect sexual desire in females   b. affect sexual at-
    traction and receptivity in females   *c. affect the pro-
    duction of milk by a new mother   d. stimulates the
    female to ovulate

55. Sexual desire in females is influenced by (p. 115)
    *a. testosterone   b. androgen   c. estrogen   d. progesterone

56. The pituitary gland is under control of the (p. 114)
    a. thalamus   *b. hypothalamus   c. medulla   d. limbic system

57. Which of the following sequences occur in the menstrual
    cycle? (p. 117)
    a. ovulation, follicular phase, luteal phase, premenstrual
    phase, menstruation   b. ovulation, follicle phase,
    premenstrual phase, luteal phase, menstruation
    c. follicle phase, ovulation, premenstrual phase, luteal
    phase, menstruation   *d. follicular phase, ovulation,
    luteal phase, premenstrual phase, menstruation

58. Which phase in the menstrual cycle is characterized by an
    increase in the level of progesterone? (p. 117)
    a. ovulation   b. premenstrual phase   *c. luteal phase
    d. follicle phase

59. Day 1 of the menstrual cycle refers to (p. 118)
    a. the onset of the growth of a new follicle   b. the re-
    lease of an egg from the ovary   *c. the first day on
    which menstrual blood appears   d. none of the above

TRUE-FALSE QUESTIONS

    A single underscore indicates the correct answer.

T F 1. The testes are circular in shape. (p. 89)

T F 2. Sperm are produced in the seminiferous tubules.
          (p. 90)

T F 3. Sperm are stored in the epididymis. (p. 90)

T F 4. Most of the fluid for semen is provided by the
          seminal vesicles. (p. 92)

T F 5. Prostaglandins are substances that neutralize the
          acidity in the urethra. (p. 92)

T F 6. It is possible for a woman to become impregnated by
          sperm even if the penis is withdrawn prior to ejacula-
          tion. (p. 92)

T F 7. The human penis has a bone that can be felt when the
          penis is erect. (p. 93)

T F 8. The corpus cavernosa contains the urethra. (p. 93)

T F 9. The larger the penis, the greater the sexual prowess.
          (p. 94)

T F 10. The most sensitive part of the penis is the underside
          of the scrotum. (p. 93)

T F 11. The female has two areas of sensitivity, one external
          and one internal. (p. 97, p. 101)

T F 12. The ovaries secrete only feminizing hormones. (p. 95)

T F 13. The cervix, the lower end of the uterus, extends into
          the vagina. (p. 96)

T F 14. The pubococcygeus muscles are found in males but not
          females. (p. 96)

T F 15. Fertilization of the egg usually occurs in the fallopian
          tubes. (p. 96)

T F 16. The ovaries and the testes are endocrine glands. (p. 113)

T F 17. The major purpose of the Bartholin's glands is to serve
          as a vaginal lubricant. (p. 100)

T F 18. The mons pubis is composed mostly of muscular tissue.
          (p. 100)

T F 19. Stimulation of the mons pubis can produce intense sexual
          excitement and sometimes orgasm. (p. 100)

T F 20. Like the major lips, the minor lips are covered with
          hair. (p. 100)

T F 21. Like the penis, the clitoris has a swelling at its tip,
          the glans. (p. 101)

T F 22. The presence or absence of the hymen is a reliable
          indicator of virginity. (p. 101)

T F 23. First intercourse for a woman is often painful because
          of the rupture of the hymen. (p. 101)

T <u>F</u> 24. Rubbing mouths together for erotic pleasure is universal across all cultures. (p. 106)

T <u>F</u> 25. Sexual function is controlled mainly by the peripheral nervous system and not the central nervous system. (p. 106)

<u>T</u> F 26. Both the sympathetic and the parasympathetic nervous systems are active during different phases of sexual arousal. (p. 107)

<u>T</u> F 27. The reflex centers for ejaculation and for orgasm are believed to be located in the lumbar portion of the spinal cord. (p. 108)

<u>T</u> F 28. Ejaculation centers are located in nerve tracts in the thalamus. (p. 110)

<u>T</u> F 29. Pleasure centers are located in the hypothalamus and the limbic system. (p. 111, p. 112)

T <u>F</u> 30. There is strong evidence which indicates that humans secrete pheronomes. (p. 112)

<u>T</u> F 31. Destruction of certain areas of the temporal lobes results in bizarre sexual behavior. (p. 112)

<u>T</u> F 32. Endocrine glands are ductless and secrete hormones directly into the bloodstream. (p. 112)

T <u>F</u> 33. LH and FSH are hormones secreted by the adrenal glands. (p. 113)

<u>T</u> F 34. Prolactin and oxytocin are secreted by the pituitary gland. (p. 113)

<u>T</u> F 35. Testosterone is the hormone mainly responsible for sexual desire in females. (p. 115)

T <u>F</u> 36. Both males and females secrete hormones in a cyclic pattern. (p. 114)

<u>T</u> F 37. The five phases occuring during the menstrual cycle are overlapping rather than disjoint. (p. 115)

CHAPTER 5

PRENATAL DEVELOPMENT AND GENDER DIFFERENTIATION

MULTIPLE-CHOICE QUESTIONS

An asterisk to the left of the item indicates the correct answer.

1. The Chinese consider life to begin (p. 21)
    a. bith   b. at conception   *c. prior to conception
    d. after conception but before birth

2. The amount of time from ovulation to conception is about
    (p. 122)
    a. less than two hours   *b. 2 to 48 hours   c. 2 - 4 days
    d. 4 - 6 days

3. The human body is composed of_____cells. (p. 123)
    a. germ   b. somatic   c. autonomic   *d. a and b
    e. all of the above

4. Germ cells differ from body cells in (p. 123)
    a. how they divide   b. number of chromosomes
    c. presence of a nucleus   *d. a and b   e. a and c

5. The number of chromosomes in the human body is (p. 123)
    *a. 23   b. 46   c. 92   d. none of the above

6. Cell division in body cells occurs by (p. 123)
     a. meiosis   *b. mitosis   c. both a and b
    d. germs cells do not divide - only body cells divide

7. In meoisis cells are produced that have (p. 123)
    *a. half the number of chromosomes as in the mother cell
    b. the same number of chromosomes as in the mother cell
    c. twice as many chromosomes as in the mother cell
    d. none of the above

8. The basic unit of hereditary transmission is (p. 123)
    a. the sperm   b. the egg cell   c. both a and b
    *d. the gene

9. The ovum is (p. 122)   a. about the same size as a sperm
    cell   b. about half the size of a sperm cell   *c. about
    one fourth the size of this dot(.)   d. the size of this dot
    (.)

10. Which of the following processes helps the ovum find the
    fallopian tubes? (p. 122)
    a. hairlike structures at the end of the fallopian tubes
    draw the ovum in   b. the fallopian tubes secrete a
    substance which carries the ovum into the tubes

c. the ovary and the fallopian tubes are connected so that ovum can move directly from the ovary to the fallopian tubes
*d. none of the above - this process is not well understood

11. DNA is (p. 124)
a. found only in humans   b. is a messenger which transmits RNA instructions   c. both a and b   *d. none of the above

12. A males whose single X chromosome carries the recessive genes for a trait (p. 126)
a. will be a carrier of the trait   *b. will manifest the trait   c. both a and b   d. neither a nor b

13. Which of the following statements about gender and conception is true? (p. 126)
*a. more males are conceived than females   b. more females are conceived than males   c. about equally many males and females are conceived   d. it is not known whether more males or more females are conceived

14. X and Y chromosomes are known as (p. 124)
a. autosomes   *b. sex chromosomes   c. both a and b
d. genes

15. Sperm can carry (p. 124)
a. only an X chromosome   b. only a Y chromosome
*c. either an X chromosome or a Y chromosome
d. none of the above

16. A normal female has_____Barr bodies. (p. 125)
a. 0   *b. 1   c. 2   d. 3

17. A normal male has_____Barr bodies. (p. 125)
*a. 0   b. 1   c. 2   d. 3

18. Embryos with the chromosome configuration XXY will be (p. 125)
a. female with no male characteristics   b. male with no female characteristics   c. female with male characteristics
*d, male with female characteristics

19. Which of the following statements comparing X and Y chromosomes is true? (p. 124)
*a. Y chromosomes swim faster   b. Y chromosomes are more resistant to hostile environments   c. Y chromosomes are larger   d. both a and b   e. all of the above

20. This chromosome abnormality has a very high mortality rate after birth. (p. 138)
*a. Down's syndrome   b. Klinefelter's syndrome
c. XYY syndrome   d. Turner's syndrome

21. A chromosome abnormality associated only with females is
    (pp. 141-142)
    a. Down's syndrome   b. Klinefelter's syndrome
    c. XYY syndrome   *d. Turner's syndrome

22. This chromosome abnormality has been publicized due to a
    supposed association with criminal potential. (pp. 140-141)
    a. Down's syndrome   b. Klinefelter's syndrome
    *c. XYY syndrome   d. Turner's syndrome

23. This chromosome abnormality is least likely to be apparent
    in one's physical appearance? (pp. 140-141)
    a. Down's syndrome   b. Turner's syndrome
    *c. XYY syndrome   d. Klinefelter's syndrome

24. A chromosome abnormality associated only with males is
    (p. 139)
    a. Down's syndrome   *b. Klinefelter's syndrome
    c. Turner's syndrome   d. XYY syndrome

25. Infertility can result from (pp. 139-142)
    a. Turner's syndrome   b. XYY syndrome   c. Klinefelter's
    syndrome   d. both b and c   *e. all of the above

26. Which of the following statements regarding X and Y chromo-
    somes is correct? (p. 142)
    *a. the X chromosome is crucial for survival   b. the Y
    chromosome is crucial for survival   c. both X and Y chromo-
    somes are crucial for survival   d. neither the X nor the
    Y chromosome is crucial for survival

27. Most hermaphrodites are genetic_____. Most are raised as
    _____. (p. 144)
    a. females, females   *b. females, males   c. males,
    females   d. males, males

28. Most true hermaphrodites are characterized by (p. 144)
    a. an enlarged phallus   b. a uterus   c. development of
    breasts at puberty   d. both b and c   *e. all of the above

29. Ehrhard (1975) found that genetic males exposed to excess
    androgen had (p. 145)
    a. an enlarged phallus   b. dysfunctional testes
    *c. a greater interest in sports and rough outdoor activities
    d. both a and b   e. all of the above

30. Genetic males with AIS (p. 145)
    a. secrete too much androgen   b. secrete too much estrogen
    *c. are unresponsive to androgen   d. both a and c
    e. all of the above

31. Genetic males with AIS (p. 145)
    a. are typically raised as males   *b. cannot reproduce
    c. are incapable of orgasm   d. both a and c
    d. all of the above

32. Genetic females with adrenogenital syndrome   (p. 149)
    *a. secrete too much androgen   b. secrete too much
    estrogen   c. are unresponsive to androgen
    d. both a and c   d. all of the above

33. Administration of progesterone to maintain pregnancy has
    resulted in (p. 147)
    a. masculinizing of the external genitals of genetic females
    through puberty   b. dysfunction of internal reproductive
    organs in females   *c. masculizing of the external
    genitals of genetic females in the prenatal period only
    d. dysfunction of internal reproductive organs in males

34. Money and Ehrhardt (1972) found that normals girls displayed
    fewer masculine stereotyped interests and behaviors than
    (pp. 148-149)
    a. prenatally masculinized girls   b. girls with adreno-
    genital syndrome   *c. both a and b   d. neither of the
    above; there were no differences between normals and these
    other girls

35. Money and Ehrhardt (1972) speculated that masculine child
    behavior in girls with adrenogenital syndrome was due to
    (p. 149)
    a. genetic factors   b. alteration in the uterine environ-
    ment other than excess androgen   *c. presence of progestin
    or androgen during prenatal development   d. none of the
    above

36. Testosterone administration to genetic female monkeys (p.149)
    a. partially masculinized the monkey's genitals   b. led to
    more activity than displayed by normal female monkeys
    c. led to partial development of internal female structures
    *d. both a and b   e. all of the above

37. Behavioral differences between normal female monkeys and other
    female monkeys given prenatally administered testosterone is
    probably due to (p. 149)
    *a. the presence of the testosterone   b. the physical
    appearance of the monkey (i.e., the appearance of masculinized
    genitals)   c. both a and b   d. neither of the above;
    there are no behavioral differences

38. Which of the following general statements can be made con-
    cerning atypical prenatal hormone exposure? (p. 151)
    a. sex hormones (e.g., androgens) have little influence on
    anatomical differentiation in a male or female during pre-

natal development   *b. gender assignment has more of an
impact on gender identity than one's genetic (XX or XY) gender
c. damage usually results which leads to poor gender identity
even if the problem is corrected during infancy
d. both b and c

TRUE-FALSE QUESTIONS

A single underscore indicates the correct answer.

<u>T</u>   F   1.   Much of the knowledge about how human life begins is
              quite recent. (p. 121)

<u>T</u>   F   2.   The ovum is the human's largest cell body. (p. 122)

T   <u>F</u>   3.   The mechanism by which only one sperm cell is able to
              penetrate the egg cell is one of the latest in a
              series of discoveries about how human life begins.
              (p. 122)

<u>T</u>   F   4.   DNA molecules with nucleotides are found in most
              species including humans. (p. 124)

<u>T</u>   F   5.   The reason we resemble our parents is that we share
              more genes with them than with the rest of the popu-
              lation. (p. 124)

<u>T</u>   F   6.   The transmitters of sex-linked disorders are females.
              (p. 126)

<u>T</u>   F   7.   The majority of spontaneous abortions are of male
              fetuses. (p. 127)

T   <u>F</u>   8.   The Y chromosome is five times as large as the X
              chromosome. (p. 124)

T   <u>F</u>   9.   The gender of the child is determined by the mother.
              (p. 124)

<u>T</u>   F   10. The embyro can survice without a Y chromosome. (p. 125)

T   <u>F</u>   11. Females are more susceptible than males to recessive
              disorders. (p. 126)

<u>T</u>   F   12. When chromosome defects occur, they tend to be associ-
              ated with spontaneous abortion and serious abnormality.
              (p. 138)

T   <u>F</u>   13. Turner's syndrome is the most common chromosome dis-
              order. (p. 142)

T   <u>F</u>   14. Down's syndrome is an example of a sex chromosomal
              abnormality. (p. 139)

T F 15. Klinefelter's syndrome occurs when a person has more than one X chromosome and at least one Y chromosome. (p. 139)

T F 16. Klinefelter's syndrome is generally recognizable immediately after birth. (p. 140)

T F 17. Recent research indicates that Down's syndrome may result when a faulty sperm fertilizes an egg. (p. 138-139)

T F 18. Older mothers are at greater risk of producing a baby with Down's syndrome. (p. 139)

T F 19. A study by Mednick et al., 1976, revealed that XYY men were more likely to engage in violent crimes than were XY men. (p. 141)

T F 20. Triple XXX syndrome is generally associated with exaggerated feminime characteristics. (p. 142)

T F 21. In general, extra X chromosomes do not bring with them increased feminization of females. (p. 143)

T F 22. Extra X or Y chromosomes are associated with reduced intelligence. (p. 143)

T F 23. Cases in which gender differentiation does not follow a complete female or male pattern are actually quite common. (p. 144)

T F 24. Ovatestes are gonads which produce egg cells and sperm. (p. 144)

T F 25. Higher than normal levels of estrogen exposure during the prenatal period does not appear to produce any degree of anatomical hermaphroditism in either gender. (p. 149)

T F 26. The Wolffian structures of an AIS fetus fail to develop into normal male structures. (p. 145)

T F 27. Money and his colleagues found that 14 AIS males were more masculine in their attitudes and behaviors than normal females. (p. 145)

T F 28. AIS males raised as males are more likely to produce masculine secondary sex characteristics than AIS males raised as females. (p. 145)

T F 29. The best solution for an individual with borderline AIS is to be raised as a female. (p. 146)

T F 30. The adrenal glands of AGS XX females fail to synthesize cortisone. (p. 147)

T F 31. If AGS is discovered at birth in XX females, they will be sexually and reproductively normal. (p. 147)

T F 32. Genetic females born with masculinized genitals due to the administration of progestin to pregnant mothers cannot reproduce. (p. 147)

CHAPTER 6

GENDER IDENTITIES AND GENDER ROLES

MULTIPLE-CHOICE QUESTIONS

An asterisk to the left of the item indicates the correct answer.

1. A person who is sexually stimulated or gratified by wearing the clothes of the opposite sex is a (p. 170)
a. homosexual   *b. transvestite   c. transsexual
d. bisexual (marginal definition)

2. A person whose gender identity is different from his or her own gender is a   (p. 161)
a. homosexual   b. transvestite   *c. transsexual
d. bisexual (marginal definition)

3. New parents describe infant daughters as_____than infant sons. (p. 155)
a. better coordinated   b. more attentive *c. finer featured
d. stronger

4. Compared to infant daughters, infant sons (pp. 155-156)
a. babble more in response to the sight of a human face
b. are more responsive to the cries of other infants
c. show a preference of human faces over straight line drawings earlier than the other gender   *d. none of the above

5. Hartley found that eight and eleven year old boys believe that (p. 156)
a. women are jealous and envious of their husbands   b. women die easier   c. women are sadder   d. both a and b
*e. all of the above

6. _____hypothesize that gender differences in the brain are important in determining how we behave. (p. 158)
*a. sociobiologists   b. behaviorists   c. social learning theorists   d. both b and c   e. all of the above

93

7. _____hypothesize that gender differences are the result of cultural expectations and conditioning processes. (p. 158)
a. sociobiologists   b. behaviorists   c. social learning theorists   *d. both a and c   e. all of the abobe

8. Which of the following traits have been associated with healthy women? (p. 159)
a. independent   b. active   *c. yielding   d. aggressive

9. Which of the following assumptions was (were) made by the developers of scales used to measure how individuals see themselves? (p. 159)
a. gender differences in the brain are important in deter-mining how we behave   b. healthy men and women should perceive themselves as having "masculine" and "feminine" traits respectively   c. identification of "masculine" characteristics was the opposite of identification of "feminine" characteristics   *d. both b and c
e. all of the above

10. _____developed a gender role inventory which treated identification with masculine traits as independent of identification with feminine traits. (p. 159)
a. Carl Jung   b. Anne Constantinople   *c. Sandra Bem
d. D. O. Cauldwell

11. _____identifying with_____traits have been found to respond more flexibly to a variety of situations. (p. 159)
a. females; feminine   b. females; masculine
*c. females; masculine and feminine   d. males; masculine

12. Of the following, the most important determinant of self concept appears to be   (p. 161)
a. genetic gender   *b. psychological gender
c. hormonal gender   d. genital gender

13. This person had sex reassignment surgery.   (p. 163)
a. Harry Benjamin   b. D. O. Cauldwell
*c. George Jorgenson   d. John Money

14. In most male to female trannsexuals (p. 163)
a. chromosome tests are abnormal   b. hormone tests are abnormal   *c. female identification began at an early age
d. both a and b   d. all of the above

15. Most transsexuals   (p. 163)
a. experience little difficulty when growing up
b. perceive themselves as homosexuals   *c. deal with the problem of having their genitals removed surgically
d. none of the above

16. After surgery a transsexual (p. 164)
    *a. cannot reproduce   b. cannot have sexual intercourse
    c. cannot be sexually aroused   d. all of the above

17. Change of sex operations for males are always preceded by
    (p. 164)
    a. psychological screening   b. administration of estrogen
    c. a six month period or more in which the applicant lives
    as a female   *d. all of the above

18. Female to male transsexuals (p. 165)
    a. report thinking of themselves as boys at a very early age
    b. report no interest in handling babies   c. engage in
    cross-dressing   d. both a and c   *e. all of the above

19. Female to male transsexuals (p. 165)
    a. begin having sexual relations with women during early
    adolescence   b. believe themselves to be homosexuals
    *c. tend to have markedly feminine heterosexual female sexual
    partners   d. all of the above

20. Compared to surgery for male to female transsexuals, surgery
    for female to male transsexuals (p. 166)
    a. is more expensive   b. is more successful   c. involves
    the addition of body parts   *d. both a and c
    e. all of the above

21. Female to male transsexuals (p. 166)   a. do not respond
    to physical stimulation of the penis   b. cannot orgasm
    c. cannot reproduce   *d. both a and c   e. all of the
    above

22. According to Meyer and Rothstein, which of the following
    motivations might lead people to seek gender reassignment
    surgery? (p. 167)
    a. a general ability to deal effectively with various life
    crises   b. a way for older people to deal with a fear
    of aging and death   c. a method of punishing oneself
    for real or imagined sins   *d. all of the above

23. Research indicates that the best explanation for trans-
    sexuality is (p. 168)
    a. it is a form of hermaphroditism   b. it results from
    prenatal exposure to high levels of inappropriate hormones
    c. it results from chromosome abnormalities   *d. none of
    the above

24. The greatest amount of controversy among professionals con-
    cerning transsexuality is (p. 168)
    a. its definition   b. its explanation   *c. its treatment
    d. none of the above are controversial

25. The reasoning used by Roger Starr, a nonprofessional, in his argument against gender reassignment surgery is (p. 168)
a. the Bible states it as immoral   b. few transsexuals express satisfaction with surgery   *c. he views anatomical gender and psychological gender as synonymous   d. he, himself, is a transsexual who regrets having the surgery performed

26. Reliable information on post-surgical adjustment of transsexuals has been difficult to obtain because (p. 169)
a. small sample sizes have been employed in research
b. long-term post-surgical access to transsexuals can be difficult   c. the methods used to assess post-surgical adjustment typically vary from one research team to the next
*d. all of the above

27. Research indicates that the social and psychological adjustment of transsexuals (p. 169)
a. improved after surgery   b. improved without surgery over the simple passage of time with limited support from clinical personnel   *c. both a and b   d. neither a nor b

28. Gender reassignment surgery is opposed by (pp. 168-169)
a. Jon Meyer   b. Roger Starr   c. Virginia Prince
*d. all of the above

29. The transvestite wears clothing stereotypic of the other gender (p. 170)
a. because s/he desires to change his/her biological gender to the other gender   b. for the purpose of attracting a partner   *c. for the purpose of arousing oneself
d. all of the above

30. Transvestism (p. 171)
a. is practiced only by males at present   b. has seldom ever been practiced by women   c. has, until recently, been viewed as a sin or disease   *d. both a and c
e. both b and c

31. In a survey of subscribers to Transvestia, it was found that (p. 173)
*a. most described their fathers as having a good masculine image   b. most reported a homosexual experience
c. most reported being treated as girls - not boys - during childhood   d. all of the above

32. Compared to controls, nonclinical transvestites (p. 174)
a. were less inhibited in interpersonal relations
*b. showed more impulse control on several personality measures   c. are more likely to have major psychiatric problems   d. all of the above

33. Research on the Seahorse Club indicated that   (p. 175)
    *a. transvestites feel like women when dressed like women but
    feel like men otherwise   b. most transvestites begin
    cross-dressing during adolescence   c. cross-dressing
    occurs almost daily   d. when exposed to motion pictures
    of females nude, transvestites' sexual arousal was less than
    that of normals
34. Most transvestites in the sample from the Seahorse Club
    (p. 175)
    a. were not married   *b. were not willing to wear unisex
    clothes   c. were anxious to be cured   d. none of the above

35. The fear of most children of transvestites is that   (p. 175)
    a. their fathers might influence them to be transvestites
    b. their parents will be divorced   *c. other children
    might tease them about their fathers   d. they might ex-
    perience gender role identity problems some time

36. The evidence indicates that transvestism is related to
    (p. 175)
    a. genetic factors   b. testosterone levels   c. restric-
    tiveness of gender role norms   *d. none of the above

37. It is unlikely that extreme gender differences in incidence
    of transvestism are the result of differences in restrictive-
    ness of norms regarding clothing style because   (p. 176)
    a. females don't appear to derive the sexual satisfaction
    characteristic of male when they cross-dress   b. females
    don't devise appareal which is typical only of males
    c. transvestism appears in those cultures with relaxed rather
    than restrictive gender role norms   *d. all of the above

38. Robert Monroe and his colleagues, in a review of cross-
    cultural research, found a tendency for transvestism to be
    more prevalent in cultures with   (p. 177)
    a. relaxed gender role norms   b. greater pressure on the
    male than on the female to ensure economic survival   c. more
    homosexuality   *d. both a and b   e. all of the above

TRUE-FALSE QUESTIONS

    A single underscore indicates the correct answer.

T F 1. Until recently, laypersons and psychologists believe
          that possessing traits and engaging in behaviors typical
          for one's gender was crucial for mental health. (p. 152)

T F 2. Assigned gender is based on genetic gender. (p. 153)

T F 3. Assertiveness in males and submissiveness in females
          appear to be universal traits. (p. 153)

T F 4. A gender stereotype, by definition, is inaccurate.
          (p. 154)

<u>T</u> F 5. The gender stereotype that men are more readily aroused by erotic materials than are women is not supported by data. (p. 154)

<u>T</u> F 6. Infant daughters generally receive more social and verbal stimulation than infant sons. (p. 155)

<u>T</u> F 7. Distinctions made by fathers of male and female infant characteristics are more pronounced than distinctions made by mothers. (p. 155)

<u>T</u> F 8. Barry, Bacon, and Child found that achievement and self-reliance were emphasized more in the training of boys. (p. 156)

<u>T</u> F 9. In the Sternglanz & Sternglanz survey of ten popular children's programs, females were more often punished for high levels of activity than were males. (p. 156)

<u>T</u> F 10. A transsexual is biologically normal. (p. 161)

T <u>F</u> 11. Jung's ideas of androgyny has a large impact on both professionals and the general public. (p. 160)

T <u>F</u> 12. Sandra Bem was the first to write extensively on the concept of androgyny. (p. 159)

T <u>F</u> 13. Surgery for transsexuals is illegal in the U.S. (p. 162)

<u>T</u> F 14. Most girls with no gender identity conflicts go through transitory periods during childhood when they express the desire to be a boy and may be labeled tomboys. (p. 165)

T <u>F</u> 15. Female to male transsexuals tend to overdo identification with the male role. (p. 166)

T <u>F</u> 16. In almost all cases genital reassignment surgery is followed by weekly therapy sessions. (p. 166)

<u>T</u> F 17. There is no good explanation at this point for the cause of transsexuality. (p. 167)

<u>T</u> F 18. Transsexuals strongly believe themselves to be members of the other gender. (p. 161)

T <u>F</u> 19. Methods are now available so that female to male transsexuals can become erect in response to sexual stimulation. (p. 166)

T <u>F</u> 20. The reasons transsexuals and transvestites give for cross-dressing are quite similar. (p. 170)

T F 21. Most transvestites describe themselves as heterosexual.
(p. 170)

T F 22. Transvestites are much more likely to have homosexual
experiences than non-transvestites. (p. 173)

T F 23. Most married transvestites have children. (p. 174)

T F 24. Most transvestites report being treated as girls when
they were very young. (p. 174)

T F 25. Most transvestites express a strong desire to be cured.
(p. 175)

T F 26. At this point, no conclusive evidence exists to explain
the transvestite's urge to cross-dress. (p. 175)

T F 27. Transvestites differ from non-transvestites in levels
of sex hormones. (p. 175)

T F 28. Males assuming female roles have been observed among
insects. (p. 176)

CHAPTER 7

SEXUAL AROUSAL, FANTASIES, AND FEELINGS

MULTIPLE-CHOICE QUESTIONS

An asterisk to the left of the item indicates the correct
answer.

1. We begin to have fantasies and feel sexual arousal at about
age (p. 179)
a. three months   b. 6 years   *c. 11 years   d. 15 years

2. The specific objects and acts we find sexually arousing
appear to be (p. 179)
a. inborn   *b. conditioned by our culture and our own
experiences   c. invariant over time   d. both a and c
e. all of the above

3. The_____model explains how a neutral object can acquire
sexual value simply by being paired with another object which
already has sexual value. (p. 181)
*a. classical conditioning   b. instrumental conditioning
c. two stage theory of emotions   d. both a and b
e. all of the above

4. You become aroused when you see a particular car because your boyfriend/girlfriend drives the car. This arousal is best explained using (p. 181)
*a. the classical conditioning model   b. the instrumental conditioning model   c. the two stage model of emotion
d. both a and b   e. all of the above

5. You become aroused to someone who compliments you on your intelligence. This arousal is best explained using (p. 184)
a. the classical conditioning model   *b. the instrumental conditioning model   c. the two stage model of emotion
d. both a and b   e. all of the above

6. Arousal acquired as a function of having our behavior rewarded, ignored, or punished is best explained using (p.184)
a. the classical conditioning model   *b. the instrumental conditioning model   c. the two stage model of emotion
d. both a and b   e. all of the above

7. You become aroused by others who punish you rather than those who reward you. This arousal is best explained using (pp. 184-185)
a. the classical conditioning model   b. the instrumental conditioning model   *c. the two stage model of emotion
d. both a and b   e. all of the above

8. According to Schachter's two stage theory of emotion (p. 184)
*a. we first experience physiological arousal and then we search for an explanation   b. we first interpret an event and then interpretation leads to arousal
c. physiological arousal and the interpretation of that arousal occur simultaneously   d. whether we experience arousal before or after an event is interpreted depends on the environment

9. When arousal is unexplained Schacter believes (p. 184)
a. the arousal subsides   b. the arousal usually remains unexplained   *c. the arousal is interpreted by searching the environment   d. none of the above; arousal can always be readily explained

10. In the Dutton and Aron study sexual arousal was greatest when (p. 185)
a. the interviewer was male and the bridge was arousal-inducing   b. the interviewer was male and the bridge was not arousal inducing   *c. the interviewer was female and the bridge was arousal-inducing   d. the interviewer was female and the bridge was not arousal inducing

11. According to Bersheid and Walster, in appropriate circum-
    stances (p. 185)
    a. arousal will increase the likelihood that a person will be
    attracted to an appropriate other, if that other person is
    attractive   *b. arousal, regardless of its source, will
    increase the likelihood that a person will be attracted to
    an appropriate other   c. arousal will decrease the
    likelihood that a person will be attracted to an appropriate
    other, if that other person is attractive   d. arousal,
    regardless of its source, will decrease the likelihood that
    a person will be attracted to an appropriate other

12. As a relationship becomes more enduring, a diminishing of
    love might be perceived. The authors say this may result
    from (p. 186)
    a. becoming more aware of one's partner's faults
    b. becoming tired of sexual arousal   *c. a lessening
    of anxiety and thus a lessening of arousal
    d. none of the above

13. The only type of stimulation that can produce a reflexive
    response in the body that is independent of higher brain
    centers is (p. 186)
    a. taste   *b. touch   c. sound   d. visual imagery
    e. olfactory stimuli

14. In which of the following species do pheromones seem to
    have an irrestiable and predictable effect on behavior? (p.187)
    a. monkeys   b. humans   *c. insects   d. all of the above

15. Bacteria that produce strong vaginal orders are best and
    safely eliminated by (p. 187)
    a. douching   *b. bathing   c. using perfumes   d. none
    of the above; odors and bacteria will be eliminated with
    the simple passage of time

16. The major objection to vaginal deodorants is that (p. 187)
    a. they are harmful to the delicate genital tissues
    b. they are unnecessary   *c. both a and b
    d. neither a nor b; deodorants are recommended by doctors

17. Response to smells as noxious is probably learned rather
    than innate since (p. 187)
    a. this response seems to be consistent across cultures
    b. young children do not appear to be troubled by the smell
    of bodily secretions   c. this response is consistent
    within families   d. none of the above

18. With respect to vision, our sexual behavior is probably
    influenced most by (pp. 187-188)
    a. specific sights on the body   b. the complexion of other
    people as a sign of good health and fitness   *c. our train-
    ing as to what is attractive   d. genetic components

19. The U.S. Commission on Obscenity and Pornography found that
    exposure to or use of explicit material plays a significant
    role in the causation of (p. 189)
    a. crime   b. sexual and nonsexual deviancy   c. emotional
    disturbance   d. all of the above   *e. none of the above

20. The Commission's findings can be criticized or might be limit-
    ed because (p. 190)
    a. it's members had biased views before research was examined
    b. none of the studies systematically examined if the type
    of pornography is related to the type of sexual offense
    c. no member of the Commission were women   *d. both b and c
    e. all of the above

21. Under the current law, which of the following criteria must
    be met in order for material to be considered obscene?
    (p. 190)
    a. it must be offensive to contemporary community standards
    b. the dominant theme of the work must appeal to pure interest
    in sex   c. the work must be devoid of service, literacy,
    artistic, political, or scientific value   *d. all of the
    above

22. The authors believe that young children should not be used
    in the production of pornography because (p. 191)
    a. children can be influenced to become sexually corrupt
    b. this practice violates existing obscenity laws
    *c. this practice violates existing child abuse laws
    d. both b and c

23. Which of the following senses probably affects sexual arousal
    less than the others? (p. 191)
    a. touch   *b. taste   c. vision   d. smell

24. Which of the following statements about kissing is true?
    (pp. 191-192)
    *a. it involves all the body senses   b. it is included
    among all societies in erotic interactions   c. it is prob-
    ably not very arousing since the lips, mouth and tongue are
    not that sensitive   d. deep kissing is more common in
    Eastern than Western countries

25. A substance that is believed to increase sexual arousal
    or pleasure of sexual stimulation and orgasm is called a(n)
    (p. 192)
    a. pheronome   *b. aphrodisiac   c. anaphrodisiac
    d. opiate

26. Anaphrodisiacs have been sought at least since the
    Victorian era (p. 192)
    a. to curb masturbation   b. to treat sexual offenders
    c. to increase fertility   *d. both a and b   e. all of
    the above

27. Which of the following substances is an anaphrodisiac?
    (p. 194)
    a. salt peter   b. testosterone for males   c. yohimbime
    *d. none of the above

28. Which of the following substances is an aphrodisiac? (p. 192)
    a. salt peter   b. estrogen for men   c. synthetic pro-
    gesterone   *d. none of the above

29. Human females differ from females in other species in that
    (p. 195)
    a. the females of most species who reproduce by sexual inter-
    action are interested in or available for sexual intercourse
    only when they are fertile   b. in many non-human
    species the appearance of blood signals a time of fertility
    c. human females are usually aroused only by one male
    *d. both a and b   e. all of the above

30. Students receive their most accurate information about the
    reproductive aspects of sexuality from (p. 196)
    a. their mother   b. their father   c. their friends
    *d. school

31. Students receive their most accurate information about the
    passionate aspects of sexuality from (p. 196)
    a. their mother   b. their father   c. school *d. books

32. The organ most often omitted from sex education materials
    is the (p. 196)
    a. penis   *b. clitoris   c. vagina   d. ovary

33. One important reason that parents do not discuss the word
    clitoris with their daughters is (p. 197)
    a. they assume the term will be learned in school
    b. they know little about the clitoris themselves
    *c. it does not have a societally approved function
    d. they hope the term will be learned by experience through
    friends

34. Which of the following statements concerning sexual develop-
    ment is true? (p. 197)
    a. females begin to masturbate before males   b. females
    experience orgasm at an earlier age than males
    c. females learn about their sexual response systems earlier
    than males   d. all of the above   *e. none of the above

35. A measure of sex guilt was constructed by (p. 197)
    a. Sandra Bem   *b. Donald Mosher   c. James McCrary
    d. Bill Fisher

36. Which of the following statements concerning sex guilt is correct? (pp. 198-199)
    *a. it is assumed that individuals who feel guilty about sex were punished to a greater degree during their childhood
    b. sex guilt probably results from one or two negative sexual experiences during adolescence   c. males score higher on sex guilt than females   d. people who feel guilty about sex report more ease in obtaining orgasm with their spouse

37. Gender differences in self-reports of arousal to erotica probably result from (p. 200)
    a. self-report bias   b. biological differences in the extent to which physical changes associated with sexual arousal are readily observable   c. actual gender differences in physiological arousal to erotica   *d. both a and b
    e. all of the above

38. In a study by Hunt it was found that male sexual fantasies are more likely than female sexual fantasies to include (p. 201)
    a. forced sexual encounters   b. homosexual activities
    c. unrealistic activities   *d. intercourse with strangers

39. The sexual fantasies of late adolescents are (p. 201)
    a. rather vague with little clear definition of sexual activity   *b. well-defined specific erotic scripts
    c. unrealistic and tend to reflect fantasies that permeate the media   d. none of the above; few adolescents report sexual fantasies

40. Masters and Johnson found that fantasies involving replacement of establishing sexual partners were (p. 201)
    a. rare for males and females   b. rare for females but frequent for males   c. rare for males but frequent for females   *d. frequent for both males and females

41. More recently, sexual fantasy hsa been viewed as (p. 202)
    a. a sign of emotional maladjustment   b. a sign of sexual frustration   *c. something that can enhance feelings of arousal and help one feel sexier   d. something that should be avoided if occasionally they are frightening or unusual   e. both a and b

42. Our sexual responses are primarily a function of (p. 197)
    a. biological capacities   b. psychological processes
    c. cultural experiences   *d. all of the above

43. A measure of sex guilt was constructed by (p. 197)
    *a. Mosher   b. Perry and Whipple   c. Masters and Johnson
    d. Kaplan

44. People who feel guilty about sex (p. 197)
    a. report more desire for intercourse   *b. report less ease in obtaining orgasm   c. are more likely to be men   d. all of the above

45. Survey research has found that, compared to males, females
    are_____interested in and responsive to sex while experi-
    mental research has found that, compared to males, females
    are_____interested and responsive to sex. (p. 199)
    a. more; less   b. less; more   *c. less; equally
    d. equally; less

46. In Heiman's study gender differences in response to erotic
    tape recordings were found in (p. 199)
    a. physiological measures   *b. self-report measures
    c. both a and b   d. neither a nor b

47. In Heiman's study of gender differences in response to erotic
    tape recordings (p. 199)
    a. males reported more arousal than that measured by physio-
    logical recordings   b. females reported more arousal
    than that measured by physiological recordings
    c. males reported less arousal than that measured by physio-
    logical recordings   *d. females reported less arousal
    than that measured by physiological recordings

48. Females' error in self-reported arousal in Heiman's study was
    explained by the authors of this book as possibly due to
    cultural training and to (p. 200)
    a. sample bias--most participants were inexperienced sexually
    *b. males' greater awareness than females of biological
    changes accompanying sexual arousal   c. the unreliability
    of self-report measures   d. all of the above

TRUE-FALSE QUESTIONS

    A single underscore indicates the correct answer

T F 1. Females receive considerably more training than males
          during childhood and adolescence to find particular
          things attractive. (p. 180)

T F 2. Sexual arousal is a complex set of responses by an
          individual. (p. 181)

T F 3. Classical conditioning of sexual arousal is not usually
          consciously perceived while it occurs. (p. 181)

T F 4. In Schacter's experiments subjects told to expect side
          effects from Vitamin A were more likely to vary in
          their self-reported moods as a function of whether they
          were placed with a depressed or happy confederate.
          (p. 184)

T F 5. Dutton and Aron found that males who expected to receive strong, painful, shocks were more attracted to a female confederate posing as a subject than were males who expected to receive less painful shocks. (p. 185)

T F 6. The mouth, ears, fingers, and toes are erogenous zones. (p. 186)

T F 7. Pheromones are chemicals secreted by an orgasm that affect the behavior of that organism. (p. 187)

T F 8. Some insects produce pheromones which are capable of attracting males for mating purposes from miles away. (p. 187)

T F 9. It appears that we have developed, evolutionarily, predilections for particular visual sights which increase or decrease our sexual attraction. (p. 188)

T F 10. The Comstock law made the display of child pornography in magazines or books illegal. (p. 190)

T F 11. Scientific evidence indicates that adults who read child pornography become more accepting of sexual interaction between children and adults. (p. 190)

T F 12. Blood engorgement of the genitals during excitement increases their temperature; hence, the use of the slang phrase, "we get hot". (p. 191)

T F 13. Human kisses are probably related to the olfactory investigations that mammals make upon greeting. (p. 191)

T F 14. Most research on aphrodisiacs has been obtained using controlled studies with double-blind designs. (p. 192)

T F 15. The authors of the book believe that the use of many aphrodisiacs can make sexual interaction more pleasurable. (p. 195)

T F 16. The Pope maintains that the sole purpose of sexual arousal and intercourse is to conceive. (p. 195)

T F 17. Obtaining accurate information about our sexual responses is more difficult for females than males in American culture. (p. 196)

T F 18. Males score higher on measures of sex guilt than do females. (p. 199)

T F 19. In our culture, it is considered more appropriate for men than for women to be interested in sex. (p. 200)

T <u>F</u> 20. Masters and Johnson found that the most frequent themes in the sexual fantasies of males and females were homosexual experiences. (p. 201)

<u>T</u> F 21. The authors of this book believe that, in general, sexual fantasies can change our feelings of sexual arousal and help us to feel sexier. (p. 206)

<u>T</u> F 22. Females score higher on sex guilt than do males. (pp. 197-198)

T <u>F</u> 23. Experimental research has found that males are more responsive to sexual material than females. (p. 199)

<u>T</u> F 24. Females in Heiman's study on sexual arousal underestimated their physiological arousal. (p. 199)

T <u>F</u> 25. Gender differences in the matching of subjective and physiological arousal can be attributed almost entirely to cultural training. (p. 200)

CHAPTER 8

SEXUAL BEHAVIOR

MULTIPLE-CHOICE QUESTIONS

An asterisk to the left of the item indicates the correct answer.

1. Nocturnal orgasm, often accompanied by dreams occurs (p. 209)
    a. only in males   b. only in females   c. only in disturbed people   *d. in both genders

2. The function of nocturnal orgasm: (p. 210)
    a. is to compensate for decreases in waking sexual outlets
    b. parallels waking orgasm, as one increases so does the
    other *c. is not known at present   d. both a and b

3. The most common form of sexual outlet reported by the majority of Americans is (p. 210)
    *a. masturbation   b. oral sex   c. nocturnal orgasm
    d. coitus

4. According to the authors, self-stimulation can function as (p. 212)
    a. a reward for good behavior or solace after a difficult
    day   b. sexual release when a partner is not available
    or inappropriate   c. a source of knowledge about
    satisfying methods of stimulation   *d. all of the above

5. According to Masters and Johnson, during orgasm, there is a preference for continued stimulation of the genitals by (p. 215)
*a. females   b. males   c. both genders   d. neither gender

6. Oral-genital stimulation (pp. 215-216)
a. occurs among both humans and primates   b. is illegal in some states   c. is practiced by the majority of the volunteers in Hunt's study   *d. all of the above

7. The_____position is useful for dealing with both male and female sexual dysfunctions according to Masters and Johnson. (pp. 222-223)
*a. scissors   b. man-above   c. anal intercourse
d. none of the above

8. Kinsey found that most English-speaking couples use the _____coital position. (p. 218)
*a. face to face, man above   b. face to face, woman above
c. face to face, side by side   d. rear entry, man above

9. In societies in which women have higher social status than men which of the following coital positions is most popular? (p. 218)
a. face to face, man above   *b. face to face, woman above
c. face to face, side by side   d. rear entry, side by side

10. Masters and Johnson believe that sexual response developes more rapidly and with greater intensity in the (p. 219)
a. face to face, man above   *b. face to face, woman above
c. face to face, side by side   d. rear entry, side by side

11. Hunt's research on married couples' preferences for different coital positions indicated that (p. 218)
a. nearly 70% of the population has never attempted a coital position other than face to face, man above
b. rear entry, man above, was the most popular coital position
*c. nearly 75% of married man have tried the face to face, woman above coital position   d. relatively few changes have occurred in preferences for coital positions since Kinsey conducted his research

12. Simultaneous oral stimulation of the male and female genitals is called (p. 217)
a. cunnilingus   b. fellatio   *c. soixante-neuf
d. analingus

13. Anal intercourse is more comfortable for those couples attempting it if   (p. 223)
*a. a sterile lubricant like K-Y jelly is used
b. lubricants are not used   c. petroleum based lubricants are used   d. lubricants which are not water-soluable are used

14. The first attempt to study human sexual response through systematic observation in a laboratory setting was made by (p. 224)
a. Freud   b. Kinsey   c. Perry and Whipple   *d. Masters and Johnson

15. Masters and Johnson focused primarily on the_____ aspects of sexual responding   (p. 223)
*a. physiological and behavioral   b. psychological
c. cultural   d. emotional and motivational

16. Which of the following sequences of sexual response was conceptualized by Masters and Johnson?   (p. 226)
a. sexual desire, excitement, orgasm, resolution
b. excitement, plateau, orgasm   c. sexual desire, excitement, orgasm   *d. excitement, plateau, orgasm, resolution

17. Before the work of Masters and Johnson it was widely believed that   (p. 225)
a. women but not men were easily aroused   *b. men but not women were easily aroused   c. men and women were both easily aroused   d. neither men nor women were easily aroused

18. Masters and Johnson found that most bodily changes that occurred in the sexual response cycle were due to   (p. 225)
a. vasocongestion   b. myotonia   c. homeostasis
*d. both a and b   e. all of the above

19. Masters and Johnson found only two major gender differences in sexual response systems. They were   (p. 225)
a. males could orgasm more quickly but only females could have multiple orgasms   b. females could have more intense orgasms, but only males could ejaculate   *c. only males could ejaculate, but only females could have multiple orgasms
d. males could orgasm more quickly, but females could have more intense orgasms

20. During the plateau phase of the sexual response cycle conceptualized by Masters and Johnson,   (p. 225)
a. the testes are at their maximum elevation   *b. the testes increase in size by 50%   c. the testes descend and return to normal size   d. no change occurs in the size or elevation of the testes

21. General loss of voluntary control in the male occurs during the_____phase of the sexual response cycle.   (p. 227)
a. excitement   b. plateau   *c. orgasm   d. resolution

22. A sweating reaction in 30% to 40% of males occurs in the _____phase of the sexual response cycle.   (p. 226)
*a. resolution   b. excitement   c. orgasm   d. sexual desire

23. Production of vaginal lubricant in the sexual response system of the female is the result of (p. 228)
*a. vasocongestion   b. myotonia   c. the secretion of hormones by the vagina   d. all of the above

24. The enlarged clitoris retracts beneath the clitoral hood during the_____phase of the sexual response cycle. (p. 228)
a. excitement   *b. plateau   c. orgasm   d. resolution

25. During female orgasm contractions occur in the (p. 230)
a. vagina   b. uterus   c. fallopian tubes   *d. all of the above

26. Which of the following response cycle patterns seems to occur in young or sexually inexperienced women? (p. 230)
a. the female proceeds through the entire response cycle having one or more multiple orgasms without interruption
*b. the female has gradual increases in arousal and a fluctuating plateau phase with small surges toward orgasm
c. the female has a single orgasm of extreme intensity with little time spent in the plateau phase   d. none of the above--a sexually inexperienced woman is equally likely to experience any one of these patterns

27. The authors of this book mention two factors that make us overly vulnerable and insecure about our sexual feelings. These are (p. 232)
a. contradictory findings in sexuality research; taboos against sharing information about sex   b. absence of sexuality research; boasts of feats by our friends that we cannot accomplish   c. contradictory findings in sexuality research; boasts of feats by our friends that we cannot accomplish   *d. absence of research findings; taboos against sharing information about sex

28. Which of the following sexual response sequences was conceptualized by Kaplan? (p. 233)
a. sexual desire, orgasm, resolution   b. excitement, plateau, orgasm   *c. sexual desire, excitement, orgasm   d. excitement, plateau, orgasm

29. Which of the following statements concerning male and female sexual response patterns is true? (p. 233)
a. both males and females show little variability in sexual response patterns   b. males show more variability than females in sexual response patterns   *c. females show more variability than males in sexual response patterns   d. both males and females show a great deal of variability in sexual response patterns

30. Which of the following statements concerning male and female subjective experiences of orgasm is true? (p. 233)
a. although professionals can distinguish between male and female descriptions of orgasm, most people (e.g., psychology students) cannot   b. the subjective experience of orgasm is closely related to the physiological experiences for both men and women   *c. professionals are unable to distinguish between male and female written descriptions of orgasm   d. generally, women are able to differentiate between different types of orgasms experienced at different times

31. Which of the following conclusions was made by Masters and Johnson concerning subjective experiences of female orgasm? (p. 233)
a. women do not make subjective distinctions between masturbatory and coital orgasm, although some physiological distinctions were present   b. women do make subjective distinctions between masturbatory and coital orgasm, but these distinctions do not match physiological distinctions   c. women's subjective experiences of orgasm closely matched physiological experiences   *d. none of the above-- Masters and Johnson did not obtain women's subjective experiences of orgasm

32. Sherfey's argument on evolution and the female orgasm is that (p. 234)
a. female orgasm is unique to human beings   b. the primitive women's weak sexual drive was very adaptive
c. female orgasm is found in some female mammals but not others   *d. the absence or infrequency of orgasm in human females is the result of repression

33. Symons argument on evolution and the female orgasm is that (p. 234)
*a. unlike human males whose orgasm appears to have evolved from lower species, human females are unique in their ability to reach orgasm as compared to females in other species   b. female orgasm is unique to human beings
c. the absence or infrequency of orgasm in human females is due to repression   d. female mammals are more likely to experience orgasm in the wild than in captivity, and thus orgasm might be governed by social norms

34. Singer and Singer described_____types of female orgasm. (p. 235)
a. one   b. two   *c. three   d. four

35. According to Singer and Singer, a_____orgasm is characterized by a gasping type of breath. (p. 235)
*a. uterine   b. vulval   c. blended   d. clitoral

36. Ejaculatory fluid in women had a high concentration of
    (p. 235)
    a. urea   *b. prostate acid phosphatase
    c. progonadotropins   d. creatinine

37. The findings on consistency of female orgasm indicate that
    (p. 237)
    *a. women who consistently reached orgasm were more likely
    to engage in lengthy foreplay and intercourse
    b. about 25% of women rarely or never have orgasm
    c. most women have orgasm almost every time they have inter-
    course   d. most women can experience orgasm without
    direct clitoral stimulation

38. The research on multiple orgasms in females indicates that
    (p. 238)
    *a. large individual differences in women's preferences for
    the number and type of orgasm   b. most females prefer
    multiple orgasms to single orgasms   c. most females
    prefer clitoral to vaginal orgasms   d. most females
    prefer vaginal to clitoral orgasms

39. The research on multiple orgasms in males indicates that
    (pp. 238-238)
    a. some males can orgasm and ejaculate repeatedly without
    a refractory period   b. some males can repeatedly have
    orgasm without ejaculating   c. most men who report
    having multiple orgasms have considerable sexual experience
    *d. all of the above

TRUE-FALSE QUESTIONS

A single underscore indicates the correct answer.

T F 1. Our sexual response patterns are greatly influenced by
        learning. (p. 209)

T F 2. The majority of married Americans masturbate at least
        once a month. (p. 211)

T F 3. More variation in methods of self-stimulation are
        found among males than among females. (p. 212)

T F 4. The typical coital position in a culture appears
        to be correlated with the social status of females.
        (p. 218)

T F 5. Nonhuman species rely almost entirely on rear-entry
        coitus, whereas humans have intercourse almost
        entirely in the man-above face-to-face position.
        (p. 218)

T F 6. The face to face, man above coital position remains the most frequent coital position in American society.(p.218)

T F 7. It has been found that women have higher status in those cultures in which the face to face, woman above coital position is most preferred. (p. 218)

T F 8. Analingus refers to oral stimulation of the sensitive tissue around the anus and anal intercourse. (p. 222)

T F 9. Kinsey was the first scientist to study human sexual response through systematic observation in the laboratory. (p. 224)

T F 10. Before the work of Masters and Johnson it was widely believed that both men and women were slow to become sexually aroused. (p. 225)

T F 11. Masters and Johnson emphasized the similarities between male and female sexual response patterns. (p. 225)

T F 12. In both men and women an initial set of orgasmic contractions is separated by short time intervals, and a latter set of contractions is separated by larger time intervals. (p. 225)

T F 13. In both males and females the plateau and orgasmic phases of their sexual response cycles are accompanied by an increase in heart rate and blood pressure. (p. 225)

T F 14. In retrograde ejaculation, semen is propelled into the bladder instead of the urethra. (p. 227)

T F 15. During orgasm uterine contractions are even more intense than contractions at the outer third of the vagina. (p. 230)

T F 16. The variability in sexual responding is greater for females than it is for males. (p. 233)

T F 17. Kaplan combines Masters and Johnson's excitement and plateau phases into an excitement phase. (p. 232)

T F 18. It appears that there are differences between male and female subjective experiences of orgasm. (p. 233)

T F 19. Most evidence indicates that females from many species experience orgasms both in the wild and captivity. (p. 234)

T F 20. Masters and Johnson found evidence for a distinction between masturbatory and coital orgasm. (p, 233, 235)

T <u>F</u> 21. The vulval orgasm described by Singer is characterized by both the breath-holding response and by contractions of the orgasmic platform. (p. 235)

<u>T</u> F 22. Perry and Whipple believe that the pelvic nerve is responsible for ejaculation in females. (p. 236)

T <u>F</u> 23. Kinsey's research contained detailed information concerning the consistency of male orgasm. (p. 237)

<u>T</u> F 24. Hunt found a higher percentage of men to be nonorgasmic than Kinsey. (p. 237)

T <u>F</u> 25. Most women have a preference for vaginal rather than clitoral orgasms. (p. 238)

T <u>F</u> 26. The ability of some women to have multiple orgasms indicates that they are sexually superior to women who have only one orgasm. (p. 238)

T <u>F</u> 27. Females whose sexual patterns do not match one of the three patterns observed by Masters and Johnson should be concerned about sexual dysfunction. (p. 230)

<u>T</u> F 28. Masters and Johnson failed to find any men who had repeated multiple orgasms before ejaculation and therefore concluded that men cannot have multiple orgasms. (p. 238)

CHAPTER 9

SEXUAL DYSFUNCTIONS AND THERAPY

MULTIPLE-CHOICE QUESTIONS

An asterisk to the left of the item indicates the correct answer.

1. Masters and Johnson estimate that at least_____of married Americans have experienced or will experience sexual dysfunction. (p. 241)
   a. 10%   b. 25%   c. 35%   *d. 50%

2. Which of the following is a psychological factor that might lead to sexual dysfunction? (p. 242)
   a. endocrine disorders   b. neurogenic disorders
   c. vascular disorders   *d. none of the above

3. Most authorities believe the majority of sexual dysfunctions are due mostly to (p. 242)
   a. sociological factors   b. organic factors

*c. psychological factors   d. motivational factors

4. Psychoanalytic theorists are most likely to explain sexual
    dysfunction in terms of   (p. 242)
    *a. critical childhood experiences   b. communication
    problems   c. misinformation about sexuality
    d. destructive relationships

5. Which of the following are remote (or indirect) factors that
    can lead to sexual dysfunction? (p. 243)
    a. exposure to misinformation at a young age   b. repressive-
    ness of the society in which one is raised   c. traumatic
    childhood events   *d. all of the above

6. Almost all psychological factors associated with sexual dys-
    function (p. 243)
    a. result from organic disorders   b. can be related to
    early childhood experiences   *c. can be related to the
    association of anxiety with sexual activity   d. result
    from misinformation about sexual functioning

7. Spectating refers to   (p. 243-244)
    a. watching erotic films but not become aroused
    b. mentally removing oneself from therapy and observing the
    behavior of the therapist instead   *c. monitoring one's
    own sexual activity rather than becoming immersed in the
    sexual experience   d. none of the above

8. The authors of this book believe that sexual dysfunctions are
    always the result of (p. 246)
    a. conflicting relations   *b. stress   c. misinformation
    d. lack of trust

9. Keller (1976) studied sexual dysfunction from a(n)_____
    perspective. (p. 246)
    a. psychological   *b. evolutionary   c. sociological
    d. biological

10. Wabrek and Burchell have found a relationship between male
    sexual dysfunction and_____. (p. 247)
    a. kidney failure   b. depression   *c. heart attacks
    d. all of the above

11. People with which of the following disorders respond best to
    sex therapy? (p. 253)
    a. hyperactive sexual desire   b. inhibited sexual desire
    *c. excitement disorders following a period of normal
    functioning   d. excitement disorders which have always
    been present in sexual interaction

12. Kaplan maintains that excessive sexual desire is usually associated with (p. 250)
a. sexual perversion *b. obsessive compulsive reaction
c. hostility toward one's parent d. depression

13. Kaplan maintains that inhibited sexual desire is usually associated with (p. 254)
a. exhibitionism b. obsessive-compulsive reaction
c. excessive masturbation *d. depression

14. The most common affliction seen among men who seek therapy is (p. 253)
*a. erectile dysfunction b. premature ejaculation
c. inhibited male orgasm d. inhibited sexual desire

15. Erections which occur in the absence of stimulation are most common (p. 253)
a. after eating b. after exercising c. all of the above
*d. after first waking up in the morning

16. The major problem with the terms impotency and frigidity are (p. 252)
*a. the terms are demeaning b. the terms represent dysfunctions that are very hard to diagnose c. the terms represent dysfunctions which are actually very rare
d. all of the above

17. Occassional non-responsiveness during sexual interaction (p. 252)
a. should be regarded with caution *b. is normal
c. usually indicates a dysfunction exists d. usually indicates hostility toward one's partner

18. For which of the following disorders is it easiest to rule out medical difficulties? (p. 253)
a. excessive sexual desire b. inhibited sexual desire
*c. male erectile dysfunction d. female erectile dysfunction

19. Which of the following disorders is most difficult to define? (p. 254)
a. excessive sexual desire b. inhibited sexual desire
c. erectile disorders *d. orgasm disorders

20. Which of the following statements concerning orgasm is correct? (p. 254)
a. orgasm generally occurs simultaneously for most couples
b. if one partner responds more quickly than another then one of the partners is most likely dysfunctional
*c. there is an enormous amount of variation from one person to the next in the amount of stimulation enjoyed before orgasm
d. orgasm dysfunctions actually seldom exist, since there is so much variation among people

21. Which of the following definitions of premature ejaculation is probably most useful? (p. 254)
*a. ejaculation occurs before the person wishes it, because of recurrent and persistent absence of reasonable voluntary control during sexual activity   b. the number of times a man thrusts his penis into his partner before ejaculating   c. the amount of time between penetration and ejaculation   d. ejaculation before the partner achieves sexual gratification at least half of the time

22. Control of ejaculation is (p. 255)
a. inherited   *b. learned   c. both a and b
d. involuntary

23. The best way to prevent premature ejaculation is to (p. 255)
a. avoid sexual interaction   b. think of non-arousing things during sexual interaction   *c. recognize signals that occur just before ejaculation   d. not try to control it at all

24. Which of the following factors is associated with inhibited male orgasm according to Masters and Johnson? (p. 255)
a. religious orthodoxy   b. male fear of pregnancy
c. maternal dominance   *d. all of the above

25. Kaplan reported that the most common sexual complaint of women is (p. 256)
*a. inhibited female orgasm   b. inhibited sexual desire
c. vaginismus   d. general sexual dysfunction

26. Which of the following indicates inhibited female orgasm according to almost all therapists? (p. 256)
*a. inability to experience orgasm under any circumstances
b. inability to experience orgasm during masturbation
c. inability to experience orgasm during coitus
d. all of the above   e. none of the above

27. The disorder associated with recurrent and consistent pain during sexual intercourse is (p. 257)
a. vaginismus   *b. functional dyspareunia
c. priapism   d. herpes genitalis

28. Which of the following statements concerning functional dyspareunia and vaginismus are true? (p. 257)
a. functional dyspareunia can be a source of vaginismus
b. vaginismus can be a source of functional dyspareunia
*c. both a and b   d. functional dyspareunia is unrelated to vaginismus

29. The disorder associated with the involuntary contraction of the pubococcygeus muscle surrounding the outer third of the vagina is (p. 257)   *a. vaginismus   b. functional dyspareunia   c. priapism   d. herpes genitalis

30. The few cases reported of priapism usually have been due to
    (p. 258)
    a. extreme sexual arousal   b. psychological factors
    *c. biological factors   d. intense emotional disturbance

31. According to Masters and Johnson, a unique, but crucial aspect
    of their treatment program is   (p. 258)
    a. having both male and female partners involved in the ther-
    apy   b. the use of sexual surrogates for patients without
    partners   c. all of the above   *d. having both male
    and female therapists

32. The major argument against the use of surrogates in sexual
    therapy is that   (p. 269)
    a. success rates have been poor   *b. they are cautioned
    not to develop any emotional attachment to the client, and
    this practice is unrepresentative of true relationships
    c. it is currently illegal to use surrogates in therapy
    d. all of the above

33. Which of the following aspects of Masters and Johnson's
    therapy program may have led to high success rates? (p. 259)
    a. a lenient criterion of success may have been used
    b. sampling bias -- those treated were good candidates for
    therapy   c. clients treated by Masters and Johnson may
    have been more ignorant about sexual matters than clients
    treated today   *d. all of the above

34. Kaplan's approach to sex therapy   (p. 261)
    *a. uses behavioral methods first and then psychoanalytic
    methods if believed necessary   b. uses two therapists as
    does the approach used by Masters and Johnson
    c. has reported success levels equal to Masters and Johnson
    d. is initially geared to resolving unconscious conflicts

35. Systematic desensitization is   (p. 262)
    a. technique used mostly by psychoanalytic therapists
    b. based on alternating between giving and receiving
    stimulation   *c. involves learning a series of muscle
    relaxation exercises   d. generally is ineffective for
    orgasm disorders

36. Most programs for orgasmically-inhibited women involve
    (p. 265)
    *a. masturbation training   b. systematic desensitization
    c. drugs and medication   d. psychoanalytic therapy to
    resolve unconscious conflicts

37. The Semans Start-Stop Technique was developed to aid men who
    (p. 266)
    a. have erectile dysfunction   *b. are premature ejacula-
    tors   c. are retarded ejaculators d. both a and c

118

38. The most commonly employed treatment for premature ejacula-
    tors is (p. 267)
    a. Semans Stop Technique   *b. Squeeze Technique
    c. masturbation training   d. systematic desensitization

39. When using the Squeeze Technique, intercourse is first
    attempted in the_____position. (p. 267)
    a. face to face, man above   *b. face to face, woman above
    c. rear entry, side by side   d. face to face, side by side

40. Surgical procedures, including implants, have been used in the
    treatment of (p. 270)
    *a. primary erectile dysfunction   b. secondary erectile
    dysfunction   c. primary orgasm dysfunction
    d. secondary orgasm dysfunction

41. Hormones have been used for years to treat (p. 270)
    a. inhibited sexual desire   b. excessive sexual desire
    *c. erectile dysfunction   d. orgasm dysfunction

42. Most qualified sex therapists can be found (p. 271)
    a. through advertisements in the phonebook or newspaper
    b. by consulting professionals in the community
    c. by consulting professional organizations such as the
    American Association of Sex Educators   *d. both b and c
    e. all of the above

43. The authors of this book believe that sexual contact between
    client and therapist is unethical because (p. 271)
    a. the therapist and the client are in a position of differ-
    ential power and exposure   b. therapists might be biased
    toward interacting with younger, more attractive clients,
    thus meeting the needs of the therapist and not the client
    c. sexual problems, including conflicts about relationships,
    are unlikely to be resolved through sexual interaction with
    a therapist   *d. all of the above

TRUE-FALSE QUESTIONS

    A single underscore indicates the correct answer.

T F 1. The majority of sexual dysfunctions are mainly due to
          psychological factors. (p. 242)

T F 2. It has been found that the more sexually repressive a
          society is, the greater the number of problems reported
          with erectile functioning. (p. 243)

T F 3. Almost all of the psychological factors associated with
          sexual dysfunction can be traced to traumatic child-
          hood experiences. (p. 243)

T F 4. Keller believes that successful sex therapy can lead to decreased sexual dysfunction in future generations. (p. 246)

T F 5. Organic and psychological factors often interact to produce sexual dysfunction. (p. 246)

T F 6. The Diagnostic and Statistical Manual only recently included sexual dysfunctions in its listing of sexual disorders. (p. 247)

T F 7. Inhibited sexual desire is usually associated with obsessive-compulsive reaction. (p. 250)

T F 8. Clients with excessive sexual desire are usually good clients for sex therapy. (p. 250)

T F 9. A person is diagnosed as having a primary disorder if he or she has not experienced normal sexual functioning at any time prior to the disorder. (p. 252)

T F 10. In most cultures men are subjected to greater pressures to perform sexually. (p. 252)

T F 11. Women's reactions to an inability to respond to erotic stimulation show a much greater variation than do men's. (p. 252)

T F 12. The most common affliction seen among men who seek therapy is inhibited male orgasm. (p. 253)

T F 13. It is easier to rule out medical difficulties for orgasm dysfunction than for erectile dysfunction. (p.253)

T F 14. Most men with secondary erectile dysfunction respond well to treatment. (p. 253)

T F 15. Ejaculatory control is a learned response. (p. 254)

T F 16. A good way to try to delay ejaculation is to think of non-arousing things. (p. 255)

T F 17. In societies in which the major purpose of sexual interaction is to reproduce, premature ejaculation is probably a desirable response. (p. 255)

T F 18. The most common complaint of women seeking therapy is orgasm dysfunction. (p. 256)

T F 19. Functional dyspareunia often occurs before and after priapism in men. (p. 257)

T F 20. Treatment is highly effective in eliminating vaginismus. (p. 257)

T F 21. The few cases of priapism that have been reported have been caused mostly by psychological factors. (p. 258)

T F 22. The major approach used by sex therapists before 1960 was psychoanalytic. (p. 258)

T F 23. Behavioral approaches treat dysfunction by using conditioning techniques designed to overcome anxiety. (p. 258)

T F 24. Masters and Johnson's use a psychoanalytic approach to sex therapy. (p. 258)

T F 25. Most professionals view contact between therapist and client as ethical if both the client and therapist are willing. (p. 271)

T F 26. A major part of sex therapy programs using surrogates involves genital-genital contact. (p. 269)

T F 27. Most surrogates are licensed by the state in which they operate. (p. 269)

T F 28. Masters and Johnson gave control subjects placebo treatments to demonstrate experimentally the effectiveness of their treatment program.   (pp. 259-260)

T F 29. Kaplan's approach to sex therapy relies mostly on psychoanalytic methods. (p. 261)

T F 30. Systematic desensitization involves partners playing roles in which they give and receive stimulation. (p. 262)

T F 31. Masturbation training is often recommended for women who have never experienced orgasm. (p. 265)

T F 32. The Semans Stop Technique and the Squeeze Technique are examples of behavioral approaches to sex therapy. (pp. 266-267)

T F 33. Most sex therapists do not use medication to treat dysfunction except in extreme or unusual circumstances. (p. 270)

T F 34. The authors of this book believe that sexual contact between therapist and client is unethical. (p. 271)

T F 35. Most qualified sex therapists advertise in the phone book or newspaper. (p. 271)

121

CHAPTER 10

CONCEPTION AND PREGNANCY

MULTIPLE-CHOICE QUESTIONS

An asterisk to the left of the item indicates the correct answer.

1. To maximize the chances of conception a couple should have intercourse (p. 275)
   *a. a few days before ovulation   b. during ovulation
   c. a few days after ovulation   d. a few days before a menstrual period beings

2. Which coital position maximizes the chances of conception? (p. 275)
   *a. face to face, man above   b. face to face, woman above
   c. face to face, side by side   d. rear entry

3. The argument that orgasm directly aids conception has been questioned because (p. 277)
   a. arousal is sufficient without orgasm to initiate processes that enhance sperm survival   b. sperm can travel to the end of the fallopian tubes quickly in the absence of arousal or orgasm   c. there is no association between desire for orgasm and desire for intercourse
   *d. a and b   e. all of the above

4. According to Shettles which of the following practices will increase the chances of having a boy rather than a girl? (p. 278)
   a. the use of a vinegar-water douche   b. intercourse in the woman above, face to face position   *c. having intercourse several days before ovulation   d. all of the above

5. The use of sperm separation methods to select the gender of a child has which of the following drawbacks? (p. 279)
   a. they seldom work   b. they are more likely to lead to birth defects   *c. they are expensive
   d. both a and c   e. all of the above

6. The method of selecting the gender of a child by doing amniocentesis and then, if desired, subsequent abortion has which of the following drawbacks. (p. 279)
   a. it seldom works   b. amniocentesis cannot be performed until the second trimester   c. abortion cannot be performed until the fourth month of pregnancy
   *d. b and c   e. all of the above

7. Which of the following is the reason that so many sperm are deposited in the vagina? (p. 275)
a. some sperm may be destroyed by acidic secretions of the vagina   b. some sperm will be unable to get through the cervical mucus   c. some sperm will enter the fallopian tube without the egg   d. both b and c   *e. all of the above

8. Which of the following statements about gender preferences is true? (p. 280)
a. male's preference for boys has been steadily declining
*b. females preferences for boys had been steadily declining
c. male's preference for boys has been steadily increasing
d. female's preference for boys has remained about the same

9. A couple that has engaged in intercourse without contraception on a regular basis for a year without becoming pregnant is assumed to be (p. 280)
*a. infertile   b. sexually dysfunctional   c. unlucky
d. both a and b   e. all of the above

10. Infertility resulting from hormonal imbalance has been treated with (p. 281-282)
a. drugs   b. hormones   c. vitamins   d. a and b
*e. all of the above

11. The Estes operation involves (p. 283)
a. removal of scar tissue from the fallopian tubes
b. removal of egg cells from the ovary so that they can be fertilized by sperm in a petri dish   *c. removal of the fallopian tubes and transportion of the ovary to the point where the tubes formerly entered the uterus   d. removal of a mature egg from the ovary and placement of it in a portion of the fallopian tube below a blockage point

12. In vitro fertilization involves (p. 282)
a. removal of scar tissue from the fallopian tubes
*b. removal of egg cells from the ovary so that they can be fertilized by sperm in a petri dish   c. removal of the fallopian tubes and transportation of the ovary to the point where the tubes formerly entered the uterus   d. removal of a mature egg from the ovary and placement of it in a portion of the fallopian tube below a blockage point

13. The greatest fertility rates occur for couples (p. 284)
a. below 20   *b. early and mid 20's   c. late 20's and early 30's   d. mid 30's and late 30's

14. Infertility in women may be causes by (p. 284)
a. endometriosis   b. varioceles   c. regular use of marijuana   *d. a and c   e. b and c

15. Infertility in men may be caused by   (p. 285)
    a. endometrios   b. varioceles   c. regular use of
    marijuana   d. a and c   *e. b and c

16. For couples in which the woman produces antibodies against
    the man's sperm, Shulman recommends   (p. 286)
    a. in vitro fertilization   b. Estes operation
    *c. the use of condoms until antibody level in the woman
    is low and then attempts to conceive   d. adoption

17. Artificial insemination from a donor is usually employed
    when   (p. 287)
    a. both the man and woman are infertile   *b. the woman
    is fertile, but the man is not   c. the man is fertile,
    but the woman is not   d. both the man and woman are
    fertile

TRUE-FALSE QUESTIONS

    A single underscore indicates the correct answer.

T F 1. The authors suggest that statistics relating increas-
          ing women's age to decreasing fertility may be an
          artifact.   (p. 284)

T F 2. Varioceles is a condition in which cells inthe uterus
          growing in the pelvic cavity attach themselves to the
          external surface of reproductive organs. (p. 285)

T F 3. If male testicles are descended by surgical methods
          before puberty, fertility is generally unimpaired.
          (p. 285)

T F 4. Studies indicate that sperm density in males has been
          decreasing over the last few decades. (p. 285)

T F 5. Research indicates that infertility in couples is
          often the result of psychological conflict. (p. 286)

T F 6. The treatment of causes of infertility for most couples
          generally has not been successful. (p. 287)

T F 7. The problems of infertility in a couple are most often
          due to the male than to the female.   (p. 280)

T F 8. Treatment of infertility is more successful when
          genetic or chromosomal disorders are the causes of
          infertility. (p. 284)

T F 9. A large number of sperm must be present in the
          fallopian tube with the egg in order for one sperm
          to fertilize the egg. (p. 276)

124

T <u>F</u> 10. It is generally agreed that female orgasm aids conceptions. (p. 277-278)

<u>T</u> F 11. Shettles has argued that female orgasm aids conception.
(p. 277)

<u>T</u> F 12. Artificial insemination by husbands with low sperm
counts usually is less successful than artifical insemination from a donor. (p. 287)

T <u>F</u> 13. Over the past decade the number of children adopted has
been steadily increasing. (p. 288)

CHAPTER 11

BIRTH

MULTIPLE-CHOICE QUESTIONS

An asterisk to the left of the item indicates the correct
answer.

1. Studies have found that human birth   (p. 305)
    *a. tends to be a shorter and easier process in cultures
    where attitudes toward sex are more permissive
    b. tends to take longer in an unfamiliar environment
    c. tends to result in more stillborns in an unfamiliar
    environment   d. all of the above

2. In studies with laboratory mice, it has been found that birth
    (p. 305)
    a. is easier for mice strains that engage in sex more fre-
    quently   b. is easier when males are present during the
    birth process   *c. is easier when it occurs in a familiar
    environment   d. all of the above

3. Labor for the average woman lasts   (p. 306)
    a. two hours   b. eight hours   *c. 15 hours   d. 24 hours

4. Which of the following statements concerning the onset of
    labor is correct?   (p. 306)   *a. most women look for-
    ward to the beginning of labor   b. it occurs in a maternity
    ward for most women   c. shortly before, most women feel
    tired and depressed   d. all of the above

5. The watery discharge which occurs near the onset of labor
    contractions   (p. 306)
    a. results from the placenta being expelled from the uterus
    b. results from the release of the mucus plug in the cervix
    *c. results from the rupturing of the amniotic sac
    d. is a signal that a doctor should be called immediately

125

6. The first symptom of labor for many women is (p. 306)
a. a discharge of watery fluid   *b. gradual awareness of
contractions   c. frequent headaches and fatigue
d. a low fever and sweating reaction

7. Most women are instructed to call their doctor when contractions begin coming at   (p. 306)
a. two hour intervals   b. 30 minute intervals
*c. 5 minute intervals   d. 1 minute intervals

8. Contractions are   (p. 306)
a. irregular from onset until birth   b. fairly regular from
onset until birth   *c. irregular at first, but become
more regular over time   d. regular at first, but become
irregular just before birth

9. Which of the following statements concerning location of
birth is correct? (p. 307)
*a. most American babies are born in hospitals   b. fewer
and fewer American babies are being born in homes
c. in Holland, increases in home delivery have been accompanied by increases in mortality rates   d. all of the above

10. During the second stage of labor (p. 308)
*a. birth occurs   b. the cervix gradually opens to permit
the baby to pass through   c. the placenta is expelled
from the uterus   d. all of the above

11. Engagement occurs when (p. 309)
a. the placenta is expelled from the uterus   b. labor
pains cease   *c. the fetus moves several inches lower in
the pelvic cavity with its head moving past the pelvic bone
d. the fetus' head first appears

12. A false labor contraction can be detected by (p. 309)
a. analyzing urine samples   b. examining blood pressure
c. analyzing blood samples   *d. placing a hand on the
woman's abdomen to feel the firmness of the uterine muscles

13. If labor pains cease, the amniotic sac is not ruptured, and
the cervix is not dilated when a woman arrives at the hospital
(p. 309)
a. she is told to wait in the waiting room until contractions
begin again   *b. she is sent home   c. she is put in
a private room and checked every fifteen minutes
d. she is given a pelvic exam, but not sent to the delivery
room

14. The necessity of which of the following practices has
recently been questioned? (pp. 309-310)
a. washing the vulva, thighs, and stomach with an anti-
septic solution to reduce the chances of transmitting

infection to the baby during birth   b. the giving of an
enema   c. the shaving of pubic hair   *d. both b and c
e. all of the above

15. The major objection which women's groups raise to enemas is
    (p. 310)
    a. enemas may cause damage to the fetus   b. enemas
    lengthen the child birth process   *c. enemas are degrading
    to women   d. none of the above; women's groups believe
    enemas are necessary

16. Labor contractions are often accompanied by (p. 310)
    a. low fever   b. headaches   *c. lower back pain
    d. nausea   d. all of the above

17. The intensity of contractions can be reduced by (p. 310)
    a. relaxing one's muscles   b. breathing exercises
    c. focusing on a given point in the visual field   d. both
    a and b   *d. all of the above

18. Transition refers to the time when (p. 311)
    a. labor contractions first begin   b. the placenta is
    expelled through the uterus   *c. the dilation of the
    cervix is completed so the baby's head can pass through it
    d. the baby's head first passes the pelvic bone

19. The major argument(s) against the use of anesthesis is (are)
    (p. 311)
    a. drugs have side effects on the mother   b. drugs have
    side effects on the baby   c. drugs may interfere with
    the development of a bond between mother and child
    *d. all of the above

20. The major objection to episiotomy is that (p. 312)
    a. the procedure is painful   *b. the procedure requires
    stitches   c. the procedure increases the chance of
    infection   d. all of the above

21. As compared to the contractions of transition, the contrac-
    tions to "bear down" which follow (p. 312)
    a. are more intense   b. are more frequent   c. are more
    uncomfortable   *d. none of the above

22. The doctor may ask the woman to control the urge to bear
    down (p. 312)
    a. so that the baby will not be injured   b. to decrease
    discomfort   *c. to decrease the likelihood of vaginal
    tearing   d. to decrease her heavy panting

23. The umbilical cord is cut (p. 314)
    a. immediately after birth   b. once all tests on the
    baby have been concluded   c. once the baby opens its eyes
    *d. once the baby is able to rely on its own lungs for oxygen

24. Once the baby is pushed out, the doctor may ask the woman to
    control the urge to bear down with the next contraction so
    that (p. 314)
    a. the doctor can suction any mucus or fluid out of the
    baby's mouth   b. the position of the baby's shoulder
    may be altered so the baby can pop out easier   c. the woman
    can bring her breathing under control   *d. both a and b
    e. all of the above

25. The process of childbirth entailing the greatest risk for
    the mother is (p. 314)
    a. the episiotomy   b. the transition period
    *c. the expulsion of the placenta   d. the "bearing down"
    period

26. Silver nitrate is placed in the baby's eyes to (p. 314)
    a. help the baby open its eyes   b. test how the baby
    responds to light   *c. minimize the chance of infection
    d. to test the baby's depth perception

27. The hospital stay after birth, with or without anesthetic,
    usually lasts about (p. 315)
    a. 6 hours   b. one day   *c. 3 days   d. one week

28. The safest and easiest position for birth is (p. 318)
    *a. head first (cephalic presentation)   b. bottom first
    (breech presentation)   c. shoulders or sides first
    (transverse presentation)   d. all of these positions
    are equally safe

29. A cesarean section should be performed (pp. 318-319)
    a. if it is more convenient than vaginal delivery
    b. for women who are over 35   c. if the mother is very
    small or the baby is very large, and the baby is positioned
    incorrectly   *d. both b and c   e. all of the above

30. In a cesarean section delivery (p. 318)
    a. the baby is repositioned before being delivered through
    the vagina   *b. an incision is made through the
    abdomen and uterus so the baby can be removed   c. the drug,
    pitocin, is given to induce labor   d. forceps are
    used to help pull the baby out of the vagina

31. Forceps should be used to help pull the baby out (p. 320)
    a. if contractions are intense   b. if the baby is position-
    ed incorrectly, the mother is very small and the baby is very
    large   c. if the mother requests that it be done
    *d. only under emergency conditions, if labor is too long

32. Drugs might be recommended to help induce labor if (p. 321)
    *a. the baby is several weeks overdue   b. the baby is
    positioned incorrectly, the mother is very small, and the
    baby is very large   c. the mother requests that it be
    done   d. previous deliveries have been overdue

33. Compared to single infant births, infants from multiple births
    generally (p. 319)
    *a. are born after shorter gestation periods   b. are
    quicker in motor and intellectual development   c. are more
    likely to survive   d. both a and b   e. none of the above

34. Couvade refers to (p. 308)
    *a. a collection of symptoms experienced by fathers during
    childbirth   b. a drug used to induce labor
    c. a rare disorder characteristic of newborn babies
    d. a new type of cesarian section delivery that is becoming
    more popular

35. Which of the following conditions reduce the chance of a
    baby surviving birth and infancy? (p. 320)
    a. premature birth   b. low birth weight   c. postmature
    birth   d. both a and b   *e. all of the above

36. Premature births are more likely (p. 320)
    a. for later born babies than first borns   b. for women
    giving birth in their 20's and 30's than in their teens
    c. if delivery is by cesarian section   *d. for women who
    have been on an inadequate diet during pregnancy

37. Procedures or equipment used to help premature babies survive
    include (p. 320)
    a. delivery by cesarian section   b. drugs to help spur
    development   *c. a respirator to help them breathe
    d. a special diet which includes certain vitamins

38. The first liquid refreshment provided by the nipples to the
    newborn is a thin yellowish fluid, rich in proteins, called
    (p. 322)
    a. oxytocin   *b. colostrum   c. prolactin   d. pitocin

39. _____aids in the development of ducts through which milk is
    secreted, while_____aids in milk production. (p. 322)
    a. prolactin, oxytocin   *b. progesterone, prolactin
    c. prolactin, progesterone   d. progesterone, estrogen

40. _____stimulates contractions of the smooth muscles during
    and after birth. (p. 322)
    *a. oxytocin   b. prolactin   c. estrogen
    d. progesterone

41. Nipple tenderness can be reduced by (p. 324)
    a. taking drugs   b. taking a warm shower   c. nursing
    the baby   *d. daily massaging of the nipples with oil

42. Milk production can be reduced by (p. 324)
    *a. taking drugs   b. taking a warm shower   c. nursing the
    baby   d. daily massaging of the nipples with oil

43. Which of the following is an advantage of breast feeding over
    commercial formulas and cow's milk? (p. 324)
    a. protection from some infections and diseases   b. human
    milk is easier to digest   c. breastfed babies have less
    trouble with defecation   *d. all of the above

44. Which of the following statements concerning circumcision is
    correct? (pp. 326-327)
    a. it leads to a reduced chance of cancer because it is
    easier to remove smegma   b. it is legally required in the
    United States   c. it leads to reduced sensitivity in the
    male   *d. none of the above

45. The six weeks following childbirth are stressful because
    (p. 328)
    a. there is a rapid increase in levels of estrogen and pro-
    gesterone in the female   b. the opportunity for
    uninterrupted conversation or love-making is sharply curtailed
    c. parents experience a loss of freedom since they must
    attend to the needs of the infant   *d. both b and c
    e. all of the above

46. Which of the following statements concerning postpartum
    adjustment is correct? (p. 328)
    a. only a few women experience any of the symptoms
    *b. it has been observed in new mothers who have adopted
    their infants   c. it generally lasts six months to one
    year   d. it is more common for third or fourth time
    mothers than first or second time mothers

47. Symptoms of postpartum can be treated (pp. 328-329)
    *a. if women are warned in advance of the symptoms to expect
    b. if mothers devote more exclusive attention to their
    maternal role   c. if the mother takes various stimulants
    to improve her sense of well-being   d. all of the above

48. After birth, sexual intercourse (p. 329)
    a. should be discontinued for six months   b. can begin
    almost immediately   *c. can be safely resumed after
    six weeks   d. can begin shortly after birth, but should
    be performed at most twice a week for two months at most
    twice a week for two months

TRUE-FALSE QUESTIONS

   A single underscore indicates the correct answer

T F 1. It is widely believed that the onset of labor is
          triggered by hormones secreted by the pituitary gland
          in the mother. (p. 306)

T F 2. The release of a pinkish discharge from the vagina is
          the result of excess fluid secreted from the mother's
          vaginal walls. (p. 306)

T F 3. Throughout most of the history of our species, women
          have given birth at home. (p. 307)

T F 4. The practice of including siblings in the childbirth
          process is highly controversial. (p. 307)

T F 5. Women who have been shaved are less likely to suffer
          infections than those who have not been. (p. 309)

T F 6. The contractions of early first stage labor are
          usually very uncomfortable. (p. 310)

T F 7. Recently there has been a trend toward forgoing the use
          of anesthesia to reduce the pain from labor contrac-
          tions. (p. 311)

T F 8. Transition refers to the time period during labor con-
          tractions in which there is a strong urge to "bear
          down." (p. 311)

T F 9. The purpose of an episiotomy is to reduce the risk of
          infection. (p. 312)

T F 10. The risk of infant mortality and maternal postpartum
          infection is greater when a cesarean section is per-
          formed. (p. 319)

T F 11. If a baby is two weeks late, the safest procedure is to
          administer the drug pitocin to induce labor. (p. 321)

T F 12. The infant mortality rate has been increasing steadily
          over the past few years since the average age of mothers
          has been steadily increasing. (p. 318)

T F 13. A baby with low birth weight at full term has potential-
          ly more serious problems than a baby with low birth
          weight born early. (p. 321)

T F 14. Postmature babies have a much greater mortality rate
          than babies born at nine months. (p. 321)

T F 15. During the twentieth century, breastfeeding has declined throughout the world in favor of the use of bottled milk or formula. (p. 322)

T F 16. Women who initially produce too much or too little milk to match their babies' needs are advised to discontinue breastfeeding. (p. 322)

T F 17. Surgery on the sex organs of infants (e.g., circumcision) is common throughout most of the world. (p.326)

T F 18. The American Pediatric Society has concluded that there is no valid medical reason for routine circumcision. (p. 327)

T F 19. Most women experience one or more symptoms of postpartum depression. (p. 328)

T F 20. The authors of this book believe that fathers should be strongly encouraged to participate in the birth process even if they express strong reservations. (p. 308)

T F 21. Shortly before the onset of labor, most women feel tired and depressed. (p. 306)

T F 22. Most women look forward to the beginning of labor. (p. 306)

CHAPTER 12

CONTRACEPTION

MULTIPLE-CHOICE QUESTIONS

An asterisk to the left of the item indicates the correct answer.

1. Which of the following methods of charting menstrual cycles is least reliable? (pp. 344-345)
   *a. the calendar method   b. thermometer to measure body basal temperature   c. monitoring of cervical mucus
   d. both b and c

2. The body basal temperature is lowest (p. 345)
   a. during the first part of the menstrual cycle
   *b. during ovulation   c. just after ovulation
   d. just before menstruation

3. Cervical mucus is most clear (p. 345)
   a. just after menstruation bleeding has stopped   b. just before ovulation   *c. just after ovulation   d. just before menstruation

132

4. According to Furstenberg, contraceptive education is not provided because (p. 338)
*a. the general approach to social problems in American society is reactive rather than preventive   b. the majority of Americans are opposed to birth control services for the sexually active teenager   c. the majority of Americans are opposed to sex education in the schools
d. all of the above

5. Which of the following statements regarding contraceptive use is correct? (p. 339)
a. the majority of young people begin having sexual intercourse with reliable contraceptives   b. decisions regarding whether or not to engage in nonmarital intercourse are often based on the availability of contraceptives
c. the availability of contraceptives appear to lead more unmarried couples to engage in sexual intercourse
*d. none of the above

6. Which of the following statements regarding contraceptive knowledge of pregnant teenagers is correct? (p. 339)
*a. their contraceptive knowledge is inadequate   b. few teenagers are eager to learn about contraception   c. most teenagers believe their contraceptive knowledge is adequate
d. both a and c   e. all of the above

7. Studies of the relationship between contraceptive use and promiscuity have found that (p. 339)
a. college women who are just beginning to use the pill have fewer sexual partners than those who have been using the pill for six months   *b. reliable contraceptive use is associated with strong commitment to one's partner
c. greater promiscuity is related to greater contraceptive use
d. none of the above

8. Which of the following conditions which are necessary for contraceptive use remain problematic in the opinion of the authors of this book? (p. 339)
a. access to inexpensive contraceptives   b. existence of reliable contraceptives   *c. birth control education
d. all of the above

9. The conscious contraceptive user, compared to the less conscientious user, tends to be (p. 340)
a. less sexually active   *b. of higher socioeconomic status
c. religious   d. both b and c   e. all of the above

10. Of the following factors, which is related to consistency of contraceptive use? (p. 340)
a. number of sexual partners   b. church attendance
*c. accuracy of knowledge about birth control   d. all of the above

11. High sex guilt females (p. 342)
    a. start intercourse at a later age   *b. take longer to
    begin using a reliable contraceptive   c. are more likely
    to receive contraceptive help from members of their families
    d. all of the above

12. The conscientious female contraceptive user is (p. 340)
    a. more likely to conform to normative values   b. more
    traditional in gender role identification   c. more likely
    to believe what happens to herself is dependent on chance
    *d. none of the above

13. The conscientious male contraceptive user (p. 343)
    *a. report more comfort when performing the public behavior
    necessary to acquire contraception   b. tend to assign more
    contraceptive responsibility to women   c. have more
    sexual partners than less conscientious contraceptive users
    d. both a and c

14. Prior to having a sex education course, high school males
    gain most of their contraceptive knowledge from (p. 343)
    a. their families   b. their peers   c. reading on their
    own   d. both a and b   *e. both b and c

15. About what percentage of unwanted pregnancies are due to
    failure of the birth control method used? (p. 343)
    a. 10%   *b. 25%   c. 50%   d. 65%

16. The major advantage of the diaphragm over oral contraceptives
    and the IUD is (p. 349)
    a. it costs much less to use a diaphragm   b. the diaphragm
    is more effective   *c. the diaphragm is associated with
    fewer side effects   d. both a and c   e. all of the
    above

17. Which of the following birth control methods is not
    immediately reversible (p. 356)
    *a. oral contraceptives   b. the diaphragm   c. condom
    d. IUD

18. Which of the following birth control methods may block
    Grafenberg spot stimulation? (p. 349)
    *a. diaphragm   b. IUD   c. both a and b   e. neither a
    nor b

19. Which of the following birth control methods requires
    consultation with a doctor (p. 347)
    *a. diaphragm   b. condom   c. foams and suppositories
    d. none of the above

20. The failure rate using condoms can be decreased by (pp. 351-352)
a. putting the condom on prior to any penetration   b. holding on to the rim of the condom when withdrawing   c. using petroleum jelly as a lubricant   *d. both a and c
e. all of the above

21. Latex and cecum condoms differ in terms of (p. 352)
a. cost   b. the amount of sensitivity attained by the male
c. quality   d. a and c   *e. all of the above

22. The major disadvantages associated with using foams as a birth control method is that (p. 353)
a. the failure rate is high   b. the sexual act is interrupted   c. foams may irritate genital tissue
*d. all of the above

23. Which of the following methods can be used without having to worry about interrupting love making? (p. 354, 357)
a. oral contraceptives   b. IUD   c. diaphragm
*d. a and b

24. The estrogen in pills (p. 354)
*a. prevents ovulation   b. interferes with the development of the linking of the uterus   c. increases the thickness of cervical mucus   d. all of the above

25. Persistent breakthrough bleeding in females using oral contraceptives indicates that (p. 355)
*a. the dosage is too high   b. one is allergic to the pill
c. the pill should not be used as a contraceptive   d. none of the above

26. Which of the following minor side effects are associated with taking the pill? (p. 355)
a. weight loss   b. increased menstrual blood flow
*c. slight breast enlargement   d. both b and c
e. all of the above

27. Cardiovascular difficulties associated with the pill are usually attributed to (p. 355)
a. progestin   *b. estrogen   c. both a and b
d. allergic reactions

28. Pill use has been linked to cancer in (p. 356)
*a. experimental studies with animals   b. experimental studies with people   c. clinical studies with people
d. both a and c   e. all of the above

29. Which of the following women are advised not to take the pill? (p. 356)
a. smokers   b. those over 35   c. those with scanty or irregular periods   d. both a and b   *e. all of the above

30. Which of the following birth control methods was most recently developed? (p. 354)
a. IUD   b. diaphragm   c. condom   *d. oral contraceptive

31. The founder of the National Birth Control League was (p. 334)
a. Emily Moore   *b. Margaret Sangar   c. Jack Lippes
d. none of the above

32. The condom has a contraceptive effectiveness rating of 3-36. This means (p. 335-336)
a. 3 out of 36 times the method is used improperly a couple becomes pregnant   b. if the method is used properly then conception will occur 3 out of 100 times, but if it is used improperly conception could occur 36 out of 100 times
*c. if the method is used properly then 3 out of 100 couples who have intercourse regularly will become pregnant in a year, but if it is used improperly, 36 out of 100 couples could become pregnant in a year   d. 3 out of 39 times a couple could become pregnant if the method is used improperly

33. Which of these birth control methods is most effective? (p. 357)
*a. IUD   b. diaphragm with spermicide   c. condom
d. jellies and cream

34. Which of the following methods is least effective? (p 351)
a. oral contraceptives   b. IUD   *c. condom
d. diaphragm with spermicide

35. The only birth control method permitted by the Catholic Church is (p. 344)
a. oral contraceptives   *b. rhythm
c. IUD   d. no birth control method is permitted by the Catholic Church

36. Which of the following birth control methods does not prevent contraception? (p. 357)
a. oral contraceptives   *b. IUD   c. diaphragm
d. condom

37. The first widely available birth control method for women was (p. 346)
a. IUD   *b. diaphragm   c. jellies and creams
d. aerosol foams

38. There are three common variants of the diaphragm, basically differing in terms of (p. 346)
    a. the type of spermicide that should be used with them
    b. where the spermicides are placed in the diaphragm
    *c. the flexibility of the rims   d. effectiveness

39. The diaphragm should be removed (p. 349)
    a. immediately after intercourse   b. 1-2 hours after
    intercourse   *c. 6-8 hours after intercourse
    d. no sooner than 12 hours after intercourse

40. The diaphragm is most effective if inserted (p. 349)
    a. about 10 hours before intercourse   b. about 6 hours
    before intercourse   *c. just before intercourse
    d. none of the above; the diaphragm is equally effective
    as long as it is inserted before intercourse

41. The IUD probably works by (p. 357)
    *a. preventing implantation   b. making penetration of
    sperm more difficult by increasing the thickness of cervical
    mucus   c. increasing acidity of the vagina making the
    environment more hostile to sperm   d. a and b
    e. all of the above

42. Uterine infection is a side effect associated with the IUD
    most likely to occur in women who (p. 359)
    a. are over 25 with children   b. are smokers
    *c. have VD or who often change partners   d. both a and c
    e. all of the above

43. Which of the following birth control methods is fairly
    effective? (p. 360)
    a. withdrawal   b. post-coital douching   c. breast-feeding
    d. none of the above

44. Studies indicate that (pp. 360-361)
    a. breast feeding causes a delay in subsequent conception
    b. post-coital douching is quite effective if an acidic
    douch is applied   *c. the amount of time from one
    conception to the next is greater in breast-feeders than in
    nonbreast-feeders   d. none of the above

45. According to the rule of 120 which of the following people
    are more likely to be granted sterilization (p. 361)
    a. women who are young and have few children   b. women who
    are young but have many children   c. women who are old
    but have few children   *d. women who are old and have
    many children

46. The leading method of contraception for couples over 30 is
    (p. 361)
    a. oral contraceptives   b. condom   c. diaphragm
    d. sterilization

47. Vasectomy involves (p. 361)
    a. altering hormones so that sperm are not produced
    b. killing sperm so that they do not leave the epididymis
    *c. cutting the vas deferens so that sperm cannot move to
    the base of the urethra   d. none of the above

48. Tubal ligation involves (p. 363)
    a. altering the production of hormones so that the fallopian
    tubes are hostile to egg cells   b. removal of the
    fallopian tubes   c. blockage of the passageway between
    the uterus and the fallopian tubes   *d. burning of the
    fallopian tubes

49. The Lippes Loop is a (p. 357)
    a. diaphragm   *b. IUD   c. douch   d. condom

50. Which of the following birth control methods works primarily
    by preventing sperm from entering the uterus? (p. 351, 362)
    a. condom   b. vasectomy   c. IUD   *d. both a and b
    e. all of the above

TRUE-FALSE QUESTIONS

    A single underscore indicates the correct answer.

T F 1. The proportion of births ending in abortion for
          adolescents is very high. (p. 337)

T F 2. Research indicates that Catholics are less likely to
          be conscientious contraceptive users. (p. 342)

T F 3. Research with sexually active college students indicates
          that increased sex guilt leads to decreased contracep-
          tive use rather than to decreased premarital intercourse.
          (p. 342)

T F 4. Most efforts to increase contraceptive use have been
          directed at men. (p. 343)

T F 5. Spermicide need only be applied to a diaphragm once in
          a given evening even if intercourse is repeated.
          (p. 349)

T F 6. The condom should be placed on a penis only when it is
          erect. (p. 352)

T F 7. The condom helps reduce the chance of transmitting or
          catching veneral disease. (p. 352)

T F 8. If a woman forgets to take the pill for a day the
          chances of conception increase a great deal. (p. 354)

T F 9. Pill use helps to prevent venereal disease. (p. 354)

T F 10. According to the F.D.A. the use of the pill by non-
smokers does not lead to a greater incidence of heart
attacks. (p. 356)

T F 11. The current evidence indicates the long term effects of
oral contraception include a decrease in infertility.
(p. 356)

T F 12. Pill-takers have intercourse more often than non-pill-
takers of the same age, race, religion, and education.
(p. 357)

T F 13. The use of the IUD has been steadily increasing.
(p. 357)

T F 14. Birth control methods were seldom employed before the
20th century. (p. 333)

T F 15. Until the last ten years, there have been few attempts
to control male fertility. (p. 365)

T F 16. Women who don't want any more children tend to have a
smaller failure rate than women who want to postpone
their next pregnancy. (p. 336)

T F 17. Birth control methods are evaluated in terms of their
proability of success (p. 335)   (

T F 18. More women die each year from the complications of
pregnancy and childbirth than from the side effects
of any method of contraception (p. 336)

T F 19. All diaphragms should be used with a spermicide. (p.347)

T F 20. A well-fitted diaphragm is not felt by the man or woman.
(p. 349)

T F 21. The diaphragm must be fitted by a physician. (p. 347)

T F 22. Discomfort from the IUD is generally greater for women
who have not had children. (p. 358)

T F 23. In the last five years the number of males obtaining
sterilization has increased in relation to the number
of females obtaining sterilization. (p. 361)

T F 24. One problem with vasectomy is that many men who have
had vasectomies change their mind about having children.
(p. 363)

T <u>F</u> 25. Generally, sterilization reversal operations have been more successful for women. (p. 365)

T <u>F</u> 26. Once having tubal ligation, a woman may engage in intercourse immediately without any other contraceptive. (p. 364)

T <u>F</u> 27. About half of women or more have a perfectly predictable menstrual cycle. (p. 344)

<u>T</u> F 28. Cervical mucus is more stretchable during ovulation. (p. 345)

CHAPTER 13

RESOLVING UNWANTED PREGNANCY

MULTIPLE-CHOICE QUESTIONS

An asterisk to the left of the item indicates the correct answer.

1. About what percent of adolescent brides are pregnant when they marry? (p. 369)
   a. 80%   *b. 50%   c. 25%   d. 10%

2. Which of the following alternatives has been increasingly chosen after unwanted conception? (pp. 368-369)
   a. abortion   b. adoption   c. keep the baby
   *d. both a and c   e. all of the above

3. Which of the following age groups has shown the greatest increase in unwanted pregnancies? (p. 388)
   *a. under 20   b. 20-25   c. 25-30   d. 30-35

4. Strictly speaking, which of the following birth control methods is actually an early abortion method? (p. 370)
   a. diaphragm   b. oral contraceptives   *c. IUD
   d. none of the above

5. Most countries that have legalized abortion have done it for the following reason (p. 370)
   a. legal abortion helps to limit population growth
   *b. illegal abortion poses a threat to public health
   c. legal abortion helps to increase the standard of living
   d. legal abortion helps to decrease the number of mentally retarded babies

6. The Supreme Court ruled in 1973 that a fetus is a person
   with legal rights when in the (p. 370)
   a. first trimester   b. second trimester   *c. third trimester   d. none of the above; a fetus acquires legal
   rights after birth

7. The Hyde Amendment (p. 371)
   a. made second trimester abortions illegal   *b. permitted
   states to allow or deny the use of Medicaid funds for abortion
   c. was declared unconsitutional by the Supreme Court in 1973
   d. reversed the 1973 Supreme Court decision and made abortion
   illegal

8. People are more likely to be opposed to abortion if (p. 374)
   a. they have high sex guilt   b. they are Catholics or
   Mormons   c. they have little sexual knowledge
   d. both a and b   *e. all of the above

9. Abortion is strongly favored by most U.S. adults if (p. 372)
   a. the mother's health is endangered   b. if the mother
   became pregnant as a result of rape   c. if it is likely
   that the baby will have a serious defect   d. a and b
   *e. all of the above

10. In general DES is recommended for the termination of
    pregnancy (p. 376)
    a. only for women in the second trimester of pregnancy
    b. only for women who have irregular menstrual cycles
    *c. only in emergencies such as rape   d. only if one is
    allergic to copper IUD's that could be inserted to terminate
    pregnancy

11. Of the following abortion methods, which is least expensive?
    (p. 376)
    a. suction   b. post-coital IUD   *c. DES   d. menstrual
    extraction

12. Post-coital IUD is a better abortion method than DES because
    (p. 376)
    a. it is more effective at terminating pregnancy   b. it can
    be used from 4 to 7 days after unprotected intercourse while
    DES can only be used up to 3 days   c. it can provide
    ongoing protection against pregnancy should the woman decide
    to retain the device   *d. b and c   e. all of the above

13. An abortion method which is generally performed under general
    anesthesia is (p. 378)
    a. saline abortion   b. menstrual extraction
    c. suction method   *d. dilation and curettage

141

14. Suction abortions (p. 378)
    a. generally take longer than dilation and curettage abortion
    b. are preferred to dilation and curettage abortions when
    the pregnancy is close to the end of the first trimester,
    or in the first few weeks of the second trimester
    *c. are less risky than dilation and curettage abortions
    d. are more expensive than dilation and curettage abortions

15. After a suction abortion (p. 378)
    a. a woman can resume douching in a few days   b. a woman
    can resume intercourse in a few days   *c. a woman should
    use sanitary napkins rather than tampons to absorb blood
    d. a woman can engage in unprotected intercourse for two to
    three months

16. The most serious complication associated with suction
    abortion is (p. 378)
    a. hemorrhage   *b. uterine perforation   c. infection
    d. constricted blood flow

17. The risk of uterine perforation in suction abortion (p. 378)
    a. decreases with the length of pregnancy   *b. decreases
    with the amount of skill of the doctor performing the abortion
    c. both a and b   d. neither a nor b

18. Dilation and curettage is preferred to suction abortion when
    there may be complications such as (p. 379)
    a. uterine perforation   *b. tubal pregnancy
    c. hemorrhaging   d. infections

19. When pregnancy is close to the end of the first trimester,
    which of the following abortion methods is preferred? (p. 381)
    a. suction abortion   b. dilation and curretage
    c. prostaglandin abortions   d. both a and c
    *e. both b and c

20. A complication of saline abortion is   (p. 380)
     a. injection of the saline into a blood vessel
    b. injection of the saline into a uterine muscle
    c. infection   d. hemorrhage   *e. all of the above

21. An abortion method which should not be used with asthmatic
    women is (p. 382)
    a. suction abortion   b. dilation and curettage abortion
    c. saline abortion   *d. prostaglandins abortion

22. An advantage of saline abortions over prostaglandin abortions is (p. 381)
*a. decreased incidence of retained placenta   b. a smaller amount of solution is needed   c. there is faster induction of abortion   d. the procedure is less expensive

23. Of the following abortion methods, which is associated with an increase in premature babies? (p. 379)
a. suction abortion   *b. dilation and curettage
c. saline abortion   d. prostaglandin abortion

24. Prostaglandins are (p. 381)
a. most commonly used to induce abortion during the late first or second trimeter of pregnancy   b. being tested for self-administration shortly after missed menstrual periods
c. used to induce labor for full term pregnancies
*d. all of the above

25. In an interview with women who were deciding to terminate a problem pregnancy, Belenky and Gilligan (9179) found that women were less likely to have a repeated pregnancy problem if they experienced greater (p. 382)
a. regret   b. anger   *c. conflict   d. anxiety

26. Most studies have found that after abortions most women feel (p. 383)
a. resentment   b. guilty   c. sorrow   *d. satisfaction

27. Which of the following alternatives for the pregnant adolescent has been increasing? (p. 388)
a. conception-induced marriage   b. adoption   c. maintain the pregnancy but do not get married   *d. a and c
e. b and c

28. The technique advocated by the authors of this book for handling children's sexual expression is to (p. 391)
a. discourage sexual expression   b. discourage children from acquiring information about their sexuality
c. punish irresponsible sexual behavior   *d. provide extensive instruction in the classroom for responsible sexual expression

TRUE-FALSE QUESTIONS

A single underscore indicates the correct answer.

T F 1. The deliberate use of abortion is the oldest medical procedure known to humans. (p. 370)

T F 2. Throughout its history, the Catholic church has been opposed to abortion. (p. 370)

T F 3. According to Tietze and Lewis, the major reason for legalizing abortion in most countries is based on humanitarian principles. (p. 370)

T F 4. The 1973 Supreme Court ruling was based on the Constitutional guarantee of the right to privacy. (p. 370)

T F 5. Recent research indicates moderate to strong support for an absolute ban on abortion. (p. 372)

T F 6. Allgeier and Allgeier found that college women, given the hypothetical opportunity to selectively grant abortions, were more likely to grant abortions to unreliable contraceptive users. (p. 373)

T F 7. If the definition of murder is the deliberate termination of life, then abortion is a form of murder. (p.374)

T F 8. Deaths resulting from abortions has been increasing since 1975. (p. 374)

T F 9. Most abortions are obtained during the first trimester. (p. 377)

T F 10. An advantage of the suction abortion method is that it can be used prior to knowledge of whether one is pregnant. (p. 378)

T F 11. All the complications associated with suction abortion are also associated with dilation and curettage. (p. 378)

T F 12. When a second trimester abortion threatens the life of the mother, and medical reasons prevent the use of saline or prostaglandin-induced abortions, a hysterotomy is performed. (p. 382)

T F 13. Pre-abortion anxiety decreases with increases in the length and quality of the relationships women have with their partners. (p. 382)

T F 14. Women who experience less conflict when learning they must have an abortion are more likely than women experiencing greater conflict to have a repeated pregnancy problem. (p. 382)

T F 15. The more men are deeply involved with their partners, the more they experience anxiety during pregnancy termination. (p. 384)

T F 16. Most evidence indicates that the availability of legal abortions leads to decreases in contraceptive use. (p. 386)

T F 17. The incidence of repeat abortion is increasing in the U.S. (p. 386)

T F 18. The single motherhood rate has been increasing dramatically over the last few decades. (p. 388)

T F 19. Most adolescent mothers do find ways to cope with the problems of early pregnancy, and do not experience greater difficulty in realizing their life plans than non-pregnant adolescents. (p. 389)

T F 20. Most unwed adolescent mothers get married within five years of having a child. (p. 389)

T F 21. Cutright, in a study across many countries, found that higher illegitimacy rates are associated with more welfare benefits. (p. 390)

T F 22. The authors of this book believe that societal handling of the problem of safe driving has been very similar to societal handling of sexual expression. (p. 391)

T F 23. Adolescent mothers are more likely to abuse their off-spring than are older mothers. (p. 389)

CHAPTER 14

SEXUALITY EARLY IN THE LIFE SPAN

MULTIPLE-CHOICE QUESTIONS

An asterisk to the left of the item indicates the correct answer.

1. Contemporary cultures makes the following assumption(s) (p. 394)
    a. a male is the opposite of a female   b. babies are non-sexual beings for many years after birth
    c. children should not engage in sex   d. both b and c
    *e. all of the above

2. Which of the following is true about research on childhood sexuality? (p. 395)
    a. many studies have been done but findings are inconsistent
    b. most of the research indicates that infancy is the opposite of sexuality   *c. little research has been done on childhood sexuality since this is a forbidden area of research   d. most of this research has been done on Americans rather than Europeans of Australian since Americans are less opposed to such research

3. A person very much opposed to research on childhood sexuality
   is (pp. 395-397)
   a. Mary Calderone   b. Kinsey   c. Erik Erikson
   *d. none of the above

4. Research on childhood sexuality was conducted by (p. 408)
   a. B.F. Skinner   b. E.O. Wilson   *c. The Goldmans
   d. all of the above

5. According to Erikson, the newborn's first crisis is (p. 397)
   a. autonomy vs doubt   *b. trust vs mistrust
   c. industry vs inferiority   d. initiative vs guilt

6. According to Erikson what conflict occurs about the same
   time as the Oedipal conflict described by Freud? (p. 397)
   a. autonomy vs shame   b. trust vs mistrust
   c. industry vs inferiority   *d. initiative vs guilt

7. Which of the following aspects of Freud's model is supported
   by research. (p. 400)
   a. a latency period from 6 to 11 years of age   b. penis envy
   c. castration anxiety   *d. the child is a sexual being

8. The theorist who was most pessimistic about a child surviving
   (i.e., developing normally) after a difficult childhood was
   (p. 397)
   *a. Sigmund Freud   b. Erik Erikson   c. Harry Harlow
   d. all of the above

9. Which of the following theorists or theoretical perspectives
   emphasizes the importance of rewards and punishments on sexual
   attitudes and behavior? (p. 398)
   a. Sigmund Freud   b. Erik Erikson   *c. Social learning
   theory   d. sociobiology

10. The quality of the attachment between an infant and its care-
    taker is emphasized by (p. 398)
    a. Sigmund Freud   b. Erik Erikson   c. Harry Harlow
    d. both a and b   *e. all of the above

11. Unlearned responses displayed by mothers toward infants
    include (p. 398)
    a. the secretion of oxytocin which makes the nipples erect
    for nursing when the infant cries   b. the cradling of
    infants in the left arm enabling the infant to be soothed by
    mothers' heartbeats   *c. both a and b   d. neither a
    nor b

12. Which of the following statements about father-child attach-
    ments is correct? (p. 399)
    a. the relationship of the father to his offspring has been
    extensively studied by social scientists   b. most cultures,

outside American, have the father take on many responsibil-
ities in raising children   *c. recently, many fathers
in American cultures have begun to take a much more active
role in caring for their infants   d. all of the above

13. In contrast to mothers, fathers who form close attachments
with their young (p. 399)
a. form them much more slowly   b. are less skilled in
responding to the infant's cues   *c. tend to emphasize
more physical games   d. both b and c
e. all of the above

14. The greatest development of reproductive structures occurs
(p. 400)
a. during infancy   b. ages 3 to 5   c. ages 6 to 11
*d. puberty

15. During infancy (p. 400)
*a. baby boys are capable of penile erections   b. genital
fondling represents a conscious attempt by infants to pleasure
themselves   c. baby boys exhibit more auterotic play
than baby girls   d. genital fondling rarely occurs

16. Parental reactions to early childhood sexuality (p. 401)
a. are negative in almost all societies   b. should, in
most cases, discourage auteroerotic play according to the
authors of the text   *c. can play an important role
on whether the child will be able to give and receive erotic
pleasure later in adulthood   d. all of the above

17. According to Erikson, when the child reaches a year old, it
is best for parents to (p. 402)
a. be overprotective of the child so it won't get hurt
b. let the child explore as much as it wants   *c. offer a
moderate amount of protection   d. none of the above; it
does not really matter how protective parents are at this
time

18. The association between dirt and genitals is likely to be
more intense, long-lasting, and sexually inhibiting for women
because (pp. 403-404)
a. the quality of dirtiness is traditionally a more serious
offense for little girls than for little boys
b. males do not wipe their sexual organ after urination while
women wipe an area including the genitals after urination
c. urination and defecation is more erotically stimulating
for young girls than for young boys   *d. both a and b
e. all of the above

19. Which of the following statements about children's awareness
of gender differences is correct? (p. 404)
a. most children cannot accurately label their gender until

147

the age of 4   b. most children cannot identify the gender
of others unless other people are not wearing clothes
*c. children's ability to identify gender differs consider-
ably from one child to another   d. none of the above

20. According to Erikson, the stage in which children begin to
incorporate criticism and punishment into their self-images
is (p. 404)
*a. initiative vs guilt   b. trust vs mistrust
c. autonomy vs doubt   d. industry vs inferiority

21. According to_____, in early childhood little girls
internalization of moral values is less complete than is the
case with little boys (p. 405)
*a. Sigmund Freud   b. Erik Erikson   c. social learning
theorists   d. the Goldmans

22. The primal scene refers to (p. 405)
a. the first time the infant opens its eyes after birth
b. the male child's apparent realization that he might be
castrated if he doesn't give up his love for his mother
c. the first time a male child recognizes that he has a
penis while his mother does not   *d. the witnessing
of parental love-making by children

23. Kinsey (1953) estimated that (p. 400)
a. most girls don't orgasm until puberty   b. most boys
don't orgasm until puberty   *c. more than 50% of boys can
orgasm without ejaculation by age 5   d. more than 50% of
girls can orgasm by age 5

24. The authors of the text suggest that parents. (p. 401)
a. discourage sexual exploration   b. discourage sexual
fantasies   c. both a and b   *d. neither a nor b

25. Observation of the primal scene is thought to be traumatic by
(p. 405)
*a. psychoanalysts   b. the authors of this book
c. the Goldmans   d. all of the above

26. If a child has been raised in a less restrictive atmosphere
and happens to observe the primal scene, the authors suggest
that (p. 406)
a. the child be sent out of the room with no explanation
b. the child be given a vague explanation of what was observed
c. the child was given some information on sex education
*d. the child be told that his/her parents are being
affectionate or loving

27. In which country did the Goldmans have the most difficult
time in obtaining information about childhood sexuality?
(p. 408) a. Australia b. England *c. North America d. Sweden

28. In response to the Goldmans' questions about how anyone could know whether a newborn baby was a boy or a girl (p. 409)
a. about 75% of the children of age 5 were aware of genital distinctions   *b. Swedish children score higher than children from the English speaking countries
c. about 75% of the children of age 7 were aware of genital distinctions, but only 50% of the children of age 5 were
d. North American children indicated less awareness than children of other countries until age 7 at which point they became more aware of genital distinctions

29. Children judge physical attractiveness (p. 410)
a. using the same attributes that adults do   b. beginning at a very young age   *c. both a and b
d. neither a nor b

30. According to Erikson, when children reach the age in which they first enter school, they face the_____crisis. (p. 410)
a. trust vs mistrust   *b. industry vs inferiority
c. autonomy vs doubt

31. On questions related to sexual play with siblings Kinsey found (p. 411)
a. most erotic experiences were with members of the same gender   b. most erotic experiences were viewed negatively
c. only 25% of both males and females reported memories of some sex play   *d. most erotic experiences involved fondling and touching of the genitals

32. During homosociality (p. 412)
a. children experience considerable distaste for children of the other gender   b. homosexual behavior is fairly common   c. children have experiences which are important in determining preferences for sexual partners of the same gender later in life   *d. both a and b
e. all of the above

33. The sexual vocabulary used by children (p. 413)
*a. indicates emotional rather than sexual hostility
b. is interpreted by parents as indicating emotional rather than sexual activity   c. both a and b   d. neither a nor b

34. Children's conceptions of the association between sexual intercourse and pregnancy (p. 414)
a. tend to be well-formulated, although incorrect, by the age of 8   b. are learned mostly at home and in school
*c. are often inaccurate and vague, involving other parts of the anatomy such as the anus and the digestive tract
d. all of the above

149

35. Most children prefer to get their sex education from (p. 415)
    *a. parents   b. books   c. school   d. peers

36. Compared to children who have not discussed sexuality with
    their parents, those that have tend to (p. 415)
    a. have initial intercourse earlier   *b. use contra-
    ception when they begin sexual activity   c. both a and b
    d. neither a nor b

TRUE-FALSE QUESTIONS

    A single underscore indicates the correct answer.

T F 1. Freud believed that it was very difficult for positive
          experiences later in life to offset destructive early
          experiences. (p. 397)

T F 2. Erikson saw development as a process in which people
          must resolve dilemmas successfully. (p. 397)

T F 3. Children are more likely to choose their fathers than
          their mothers as play partners once they reach the age
          of eighteen months. (p. 399)

T F 4. Young children, it appears, are able to distinguish
          sexual feelings and experiences from other sensations
          and activities. (p. 400)

T F 5. For a brief time after birth, infants show several
          signs associated with reproductive maturity. (p. 400)

T F 6. Nonverbal communication is very important in children's
          sensual development. (p. 400)

T F 7. It appears that infants fantasize in an attempt to bring
          about erection or vaginal lubrication. (p. 401)

T F 8. Infants under one year of age have been observed
          masturbating. (p. 401)

T F 9. Most children reveal a marked curiosity about sexuality.
          (p. 401)

T F 10. Kinsey estimated that most girls can orgasm by the age
          of five. (p. 401)

T F 11. The Goldman's research supports Freud's theory of an
          Oedipal conflict. (p. 409)

T F 12. Most children do not begin to attend to physical
          attractiveness until age seven. (p. 410)

T <u>F</u> 13. Coital-positioning play is often observed in young monkeys but has never been observed in young children. (p. 410)

T <u>F</u> 14. It appears that sexual play in children derives from the experience of sexual pleasure. (p. 411)

<u>T</u> F 15. Sharp differentiation of masculine and feminine roles are facilitated by close association with the same gender peers in late childhood. (p. 412)

T <u>F</u> 16. College students in human sexuality courses tend to be less tolerant of a variety of sexual behavior for others than they are of those same sexual behaviors for themselves. (p. 415)

<u>T</u> F 17. From birth on, female babies can lubricate vaginally. (p. 400)

<u>T</u> F 18. Most students today receive little or no sex education in grade school or junior high. (p. 415)

CHAPTER 15

ADOLESCENCE AND YOUNG ADULTHOOD

MULTIPLE-CHOICE QUESTIONS

An asterisk to the left of the item indicates the correct answer.

1. According to Erikson, the challenge of adolescence involves (p. 419)
   a. trust vs mistrust   *b. identity vs role confusion
   c. industry vs inferiority   c. autonomy vs doubt

2. Freud's theorizing about adolescence emphasizes (p. 420)
   *a. biological factors   b. social factors
   c. the learning of sexual roles and scripts   d. all of the above

3. Which of the following biological events first occurs during puberty? (p. 421)
   a. the capability to experience orgasm   b. the capability to release mature germ cells   c. the growth of pubic hair between the legs and under the arms   *d. both b and c
   e. all of the above

4. The production of_____increases in males during puberty.
   (p. 421)   a. estrogen   *b. testosterone   c. progesterone
   d. both a and c   d. all of the above

151

5. Which of the following hypotheses about menstruation is strongly supported by data? (pp. 423–428)
a. secular decline hypothesis   b. the menstrual madness hypothesis   c. menstrual synchrony hypothesis
*d. none of the above

6. Toxic shock syndrome has been associated with the use of (p. 422)
a. the birth control pill   *b. tampons   c. sanitary napkins   d. the IUD

7. Toxic shock syndrome (p. 422)
a. was first discovered about fifty years ago when Tampax was marketed   b. is more prevalent in primitive cultures than in the U.S.   c. is more likely to affect men than women   *d. remains uncured

8. The secular decline hypothesis states that (p. 423)
a. changes in mood are caused by fluctuations in hormones associated with phases of the menstrual cycle
b. menstrual cycles of women living in close proximity to one another become synchronized   *c. the age of first menstruation has been declining rather dramatically over the past 140 years   d. changes in mental ability are caused by fluctuations in hormones associated with phases of the menstrual cycle

9. The conclusions reached by Tanner on the declining age of menarche have been questioned because of (p. 425)
a. self-report bias   b. volunteer bias   c. nonresponse bias   *d. nonrepresentative samples

10. The data on the menstrual madness hypothesis suggest (pp. 425–427)
a. the causal link between phases of the menstrual cycle and various body and emotional fluctuations   *b. more traditional Jewish and Catholic women are more likely to experience menstrual distress   c. younger girls report greater expectation of severe fluctuations than older girls
d. all of the above

11. Symptoms of male pubescence include (pp. 428–429)
a. acne   b. cracking voice   c. nocturnal emissions
d. both b and c   *e. all of the above

12. Girls tend to learn about masturbation from (p. 430)
a. parents   b. peers   *c. accidental self-discovery
d. sex education classes

13. Boys tend to learn about masturbation from (p. 430)
a. parents   *b. peers   c. accidental self-discovery
d. sex education classes

14. The results from Kinsey and Hunt's surveys indicate that
    (p. 430)
    a. girls appear to engage in masturbation or admit to it
    equally as often as boys   b. males and females begin
    masturbating at a later age than they did a quarter of a
    century ago   c. masturbation is accompanied by more
    anxiety and guilt than it was a quarter of a century ago
    *d. there has been a significant increase in the incidence
    of masturbation at all ages between 12 and 20 among girls

15. Most adolescents (p. 431)
    a. begin dating at age 14 or 15   b. have engaged in
    genital fondling by age 15   *c. are concerned with be-
    coming competent at kissing at ages 12 or 13
    d. have had intercourse by age 16

16. During early adolescence, same gender sexual interaction
    (p. 431)
    a. occurs for most teenagers   *b. is more common for males
    than females   c. is more common for college students than
    non-college students   d. both b and c   e. all of the
    above

17. A strong relationship between educational level and sexual
    repertoire was found by (p. 432)
    *a. Kinsey   b. Hunt   c. Delamater and MacCorquadale
    d. Sorenson

18. Which of the following statements concerning the acceptance
    of premarital expression over the past few generations is
    correct? (p. 432)
    a. men's acceptance of premarital sexual expression has
    increased more than women's acceptance
    *b. women's acceptance of premarital sexual expression has
    increased more than men's acceptance   c. both men's
    and women's acceptance of premarital sexual expression has
    remained unchanged   d. the majority of young people
    believe that women, more than men, should initiate sexual
    expression

19. McCormick found that, when presented with strategies to
    have or avoid sexual intimacy, young men and women rated
    (pp. 433-434)
    *a. strategies to have sexual intimacy as primarily employed
    by men rather than women   b. strategies to avoid having
    sexual intimacy as primarily employed by men rather than women
    c. strategies to have sexual intimacy as equally likely to
    be employed by men and women   d. strategies to avoid
    having sexual intimacy as equally likely to be employed by
    men and women

20. According to John Gagnon, which of the following characterizes the first act of heterosexual intercourse for a couple in their teens? (p. 435)
a. it is most likely to occur on a couch or in the back seat of a car   b. it is unlikely that both will experience orgasm   *c. the experience will be somewhat awkward
d. none of the above

21. Traditional assumptions about differences between male and female sexuality include (p. 436)
a. the purpose of marriage is to have sex   b. men want sex more than women do   c. women who engage in nonmarital intercourse should not be respected   *d. all of the above

22. Only a small number of couples in Peplau et al.'s (1977) longitudinal study were_____in their views. (p. 436)
*a. sexually traditional   b. sexually moderate
c. sexually liberal   d. sexually moderate or liberal

23. Compared to couples who had coitus within a month, couples who choose to wait longer before having coitus in the Peplau et al.'s (1977) study (p. 438)
a. reported feeling closer to their partner   b. were more likely to report being in love   c. gave higher estimates of the probability of marrying their partner
*d. all of the above

24. In early coitus couples,_____reported_____satisfaction than_____than in later coitus couples in the Peplau et al.'s (1977) study (p. 438)
a. men; greater; women   b. men; less; women
*c. women; greater; men   d. women; less; men

25. Early coitus couples in the Peplau et al. (1977) study (p. 438)
*a. were more experienced that later coitus couples
b. felt more guilt over their sexual intimacy than later coitus couples   c. were more likely to break up than later coitus couples   d. all of the above

26. About____percent of Americans marry and about_____of these couples get divorced? (p. 438)
a. 75%, 40%   *b. 90%, 40%   c. 75%, 25%   d. 90%, 24%

27. According to Erikson, the critical challenge of young adulthood is (p. 439)
a. trust vs mistrust   *b. intimacy vs isolation
c. autonomy vs doubt   d. industry vs inferiority

154

28. Numerous studies have shown that_____hold more equalitarian attitudes concerning male and female roles in marriage than do their older counterparts. (p. 440)
a. younger men but not younger men   b. younger women but not younger men   *c. both younger men and younger women
d. neither younger men nor younger women

29. Which of the following statistics is on the rise? (p. 440)
a. the age at which couples get married   b. the percentage of couples that get divorced   c. the percentage of married men and women who are choosing to remain single
d. both a and b   *e. all of the above

30. According to a study by Diane Phillis (1981), what particular type of woman remains single for a longer period of time before getting married? (p. 440)
a. women with a lot of schooling (graduate students)
b. women with a moderate amount of schooling (completed bachelor's degrees)   c. women with little schooling (less than 5 years) beyond high school   d. both a and b
*e. both a and c

31. Which of the following stereotypes is associated with singlehood? (p. 441)
a. swinger   b. reject   c. homosexual   *d. all of the above

32. In order to reduce the divorce rate Margaret Mead recommended that (p. 441)
a. cohabitation be made legal   b. cohabitation be made mandatory   *c. society accept the licensing of "trial marriage" including cohabitation   d. the minimum age for marriage be raised

33. Compared to non-cohabitating couples, cohabiting couples (p. 442)
*a. engage in more diverse sexual activities   b. rated themselves as less attractive   c. were more likely to have self-ratings discrepant from ratings of themselves by peers   d. were more traditional

34. Cohabiting women (p. 442)
a. are less likely to get divorced   b. have stronger religious preferences than non-cohabiting women
*c. rate themselves higher on leadership qualities than non-cohabiting women   d. are more introverted than non-cohabiting women

35. The authors of the text recommend cohabitation to (p. 442)
a. reduce the divorce rate   b. avoid legal problems
c. determine sexual compatability   d. all of the above
*e. none of the above

155

36. Which of the following statements about love, mate selection, and marriage is correct? (p. 443)
a. women tend to fall in love more readily than men
b. men tend to fall out of love more readily than women
*c. women are more likely to end a relationship that seems ill-fated   d. men are better able to cope with the end of a relationship than are women

37. Young people who hold egalitarian attitudes or androgynous identities (p. 445)
a. have more children   b. have children at a younger age
c. are more likely to get divorced   *d. none of the above

38. In interviews with over 2000 women, Cherlin found that (p. 447)
*a. couples with preschool children are less likely to separate and divorce than couples with no children
b. having children increases the divorce rate   c. having children increases the divorce rate   d. couples with children beyond preschool are less likely to separate and divorce than couples with no children

39. Which of the following types of mothers or fathers were found to have more egalitarian attitudes about division of labor in a marriage? (p. 449)
*a. men and women that are more educated   b. women that are more religious   c. women that are older
d. women that have not had premarital sex

40. Which of the following statements about marriage and sexual intimacy is correct? (p. 450)
a. couples make love less frequently early on in the marriage
b. couples with large families like sex more than couples with fewer children   *c. the arrival of babies is usually followed by a decrease in the frequency of coitus
d. couples with children tend to be more efficient about sex

41. Couples in which partners masturbate in addition to having coitus (p. 450)
a. have a less satisfying marital relationship   *b. have coitus more frequently   c. have problems and should seek therapy   d. both a and c   e. all of the above

TRUE-FALSE QUESTIONS

A single underscore indicates the correct answer.

T F 1. Thirteen year old teenagers report that adolescence is the best time to live. (p. 419)

T F 2. Freud's belief that adolescence is a time of great sexual interest and activity appears to be incorrect. (p. 419)

156

T <u>F</u> 3. During adolescence, sexual scripts are usually vague and simple-minded. (p. 420)

<u>T</u> F 4. The onset of sexual maturation occurs earlier for girls than for boys. (p. 420)

<u>T</u> F 5. The acquisition of reproductive capacity is more apparent to female adolescents than to male adolescents. (p. 421)

T <u>F</u> 6. There is strong evidence which indicates that males experience reproductive cycles just as females do. (p. 421)

<u>T</u> F 7. Prior to puberty, estrogen levels, as measured by urine samples, are equal in boys and girls. (p. 421)

<u>T</u> F 8. The majority of menstruating American females use sanitary napkins rather than tampons. (p. 422)

<u>T</u> F 9. In one study, women exposed to the underarm odor of a stranger had their menstrual cycles become synchronized with that of the stranger. (p. 428)

<u>T</u> F 10. Masturbation is more prevalent and accompanied by less anxiety and guilt than it was twenty-five years ago. (p. 430)

<u>T</u> F 11. By age twenty, the majority of boys and girls have engaged in sexual intercourse and a variety of other sexual activities. (p. 431)

T <u>F</u> 12. The authors of the book agree with the viewpoint that increased adolescent sexual activity is symptomatic of a decline in family values. (p. 431)

T <u>F</u> 13. Recent evidence suggests a strong relationship between educational level and sexual repetoire. (p. 432)

T <u>F</u> 14. Recent research strongly suggests that the double standard is dead. (p. 433)

T <u>F</u> 15. According to Erikson, the best way to resolve the intimacy-isolation crisis encountered in young adulthood is to marry. (p. 439)

T <u>F</u> 16. Peplau found that couples who abstained from intercourse were less likely to stay together for a long period of time. (p. 438)

T F 17. The majority of Americans approve of sexual intimacy in the context of an affectionate, but not necessarily marital relationship. (p. 438)

T F 18. The proportion of one person households in the U.S. is sharply on the rise. (p. 440)

T F 19. Even today, uninhibited sexual interest is often acceptable in men whereas women are still expected to behave much more modestly about sexuality. (p. 441)

T F 20. Cohabiting students expect to marry at a younger age than non-cohabiting students. (p. 442)

T F 21. Most people who cohabit describe the relationship as a planned "trial" marriage leading to a subsequent wedding. (p. 442)

T F 22. Cohabiting men tend to be exploitative and cohabiting women tend to be seductive. (p. 442)

T F 23. Newcomb and Bentler (1980) found more similarities than differences among cohabiting and non-cohabiting couples. (p. 442)

T F 24. Cohabitation, unlike marriage, enables couples to avoid legal complications in case the relationship breaks up. (p. 443)

T F 25. Most young men and women are still forming intimate relationships, marrying, and having their first child before they reach the age of twenty-five. (p. 446)

T F 26. After marriage, couples tend to have their first child within two years on the average. (p. 446)

T F 27. The assumption that having children provides a couple with an enormously strong tie to one another appears to be correct. (p. 447)

T F 28. Over half of American mothers with children under six are employed outside the home. (p. 448)

CHAPTER 16

ADULTHOOD AND AGING

MULTIPLE-CHOICE QUESTIONS

An asterisk to the left of the item indicates the correct answer.

1. Which of the following statements about prostitution is correct? (p. 465)
    a. prostitution is an easy activity to define or categorize
    b. prostitution is a relatively recent phenomenon--within the last 500 years   *c. every state in the country has laws regulating prostitution   d. none of the above

2. A majority of people prosecuted for prostitution are (p.466)
    a. female   b. black   c. streetwalkers   d. both a and c
    *e. all of the above

3. Which of the following statements concerning prostitution and the law is correct? (p. 466)
    a. patronizing a prostitute is illegal in all states
    b. enforcement of the laws is fairly consistent from one locality to the next   *c. prostitutes spend very little time in jail   d. the customer is usually implicated for his or her contribution to prostitution

4. Which of the following activities related to prostitution is illegal? (p. 465)
    a. operating a brothel   b. pandering   *c. both a and b
    d. neither a nor b

5. Which of the following statements concerning pimping is true? (p. 466)
    a. the punishment for pimping is less severe than that for prostitution   *b. few pimps are arrested or prosecuted
    c. both a and b   d. neither a nor b

6. The highest rung of the ladder in the hierarchy of prostitution is (p. 469)
    a. streetwalker   *b. call girl   c. bar and hotel prostitutes   d. women at massage parlors

7. The most frequent sexual activity provided by escort service is (pp. 468-469)
    *a. massage   b. oral sex   c. coitus   d. all of these activities are offered very frequently

8. _____charge the cheapest price for sex. (p. 467)
    a. call girls   *b. streetwalkers   c. hotel and bar girls
    d. the price of sex is similar when offered by any of the above

9. Which of the following types of prostitutes frequently find themselves in competition with amateurs? (p. 468)
a. call girls   b. streetwalkers   *c. hotel and bar girls
d. girls in massage parlors

10. Which of the following types of prostitutes is most likely to work with a pimp? (p. 467)
a. call girls   *b. streetwalkers   c. hotel and bar girls
d. girls in massage parlors

11. Most sex research on adulthood and aging is (p. 479)
*a. crossectional research   b. longitudinal research
c. experimental research   d. both a and c
e. all of the above

12. Most subjects in sex research have been in   (p. 453)
a. early childhood   *b. late adolescence
c. middle age   d. old age

13. The limited attention given to people beyond early adulthood is probably due to (pp. 453-454)
a. the human species inexperience with aging   b. beliefs about the purposes of sex   c. beliefs about women's sexuality   *d. all of the above

14. As people get older (p. 453)
*a. their sexual attitudes and behaviors become more diverse
b. they engage in sex more often   c. their personalities become more alike   d. none of the above

15. Which of the following statements concerning life expectancy is correct? (p. 454)
*a. old age is a relatively new phenomenon   b. men live longer than women   c. life expectancy increased up to 1970 and has now begun to decline   d. most women are able to reproduce until they die

16. A 1979 survey of employment of actors and actresses undertaken by the Screen Actors Guild revealed (p. 454)
a. there are more older actresses than older actors
*b. older actors are paid more than older actresses
c. older actresses work more hours than older actors
d. there are more young actors than actresses

17. The 1979 survey undertaken by the Screen Actors Guild is evidence for (p. 454)
a. the stereotype that both men and women are sexless beyond middle age   *b. the double standard of aging
c. the fact that most older people are women   d. the perceived decline of male sexuality

18. Older women's sexual value or attractiveness is traditionally defined by their (p. 454)
a. power   b. status   *c. physical characteristics
d. both a and b

19. The authors attribute the double standard of aging to (p. 454)
a. the media's portrayal of male and female sexuality
b. increased life expectancy beyond reproductive capacity
c. inaccurate information about sexuality and aging
*d. all of the above

20. Most adult sexual expression involves (p. 455)
a. sexual partners before marriage   b. extramarital affairs
*c. one's marital partner   d. sexual partners after divorce, separation or death of a spouse

21. The most important quality for marital happiness regarding the sexual realm in Hunt's (1974) study was (p. 455)
a. frequent sex   b. absence of sexual dysfunction
*c. agreement in sexual desires   d. the amount of variation in sexual activity

22. In assessing making love vs. making war, Howard and Dawes (1976) found that marital happiness was most strongly associated with (p. 456)
a. the frequency of sex   b. absence of fighting
*c. the degree to which the frequency of sex was greater or less than the frequency of fighting   d. there was no relationship among frequency of sex, absence of fighting, or marital happiness

23. In the Carnegie study in England of cases seen by marriage counselors it was found that (p. 456)
a. for those married less than 3 years, sexual problems were a rare complaint   b. for those married over 18 years, sexual problems were the most frequent complaint
c. sexual problems had a much greater impact on the quality of marital relationships in middle age couples in comparison to younger couples   *d. sexual problems had a much greater impact on the quality of marital relationships in middle age couples in comparison to older couples

24. According to Troll and Smith (1976) in a long term relationship_____and_____lead to shifts in the importance of sexuality. (p. 456)
a. increases in attraction; increases in attachment
b. increases in attraction; decreases in attachment
*c. decreases in attraction; increases in attachment
d. decreases in attraction; decreases in attachment

25. In early adulthood_____appear(s) to be important (p. 456)
    *a. sexual intimacy   b. affection   c. loyalty
    d. all of the above

26. Which of the following stereotypes is best supported by
    available evidence? (p. 457)
    a. sexuality is an activity limited to the young
    *b. males are directed toward sexual variety to a greater
    degree than are females   c. men are better able to
    handle the end of a relationship than are women
    d. women fall in love more quickly than men

27. Traupmann and Hatfield found that in marriage both men and
    women (p. 457)
    a. report men are getting the better deal   b. agree that
    men contribute less than women   c. agree that men get
    more out of marriage than women   d. both a and c
    *e. all of the above

28. Little research is available on extramarital affairs concern-
    ing (p. 458)
    a. Americans' attitudes   b. the proportion of people
    engaging in the activity   *c. the reasons for engag-
    ing or avoiding the activity   d. all of the above

29. Research indicates that attitudes and behavior concerning
    extramarital sex are as follows: (p. 458)
    a. most Americans disapprove and don't do it   *b. most
    Americans disapprove but do it   c. most Americans approve
    but don't do it   d. most Americans approve and do it

30. Extramarital sex most typically involves (p. 458)
    a. group marriage   b. mate swapping   c. swingers
    *d. covert relations with another partner

31. Hunt found extramarital affairs to be most common among
    (p. 458)
    a. teenagers   *b. people aged 20-24   c. middle aged
    d. elderly

32. Kinsey (1953) found   (p. 458)
    *a. men are more likely to be involved in extramarital
    affairs   b. women are more likely to perceive such
    affairs as destructive   c. both a and b
    d. neither a nor b

33. Which of the following statements is supported by data?
    (pp. 458-461)
    a. members of unhappy marriages are more likely to become
    engaged in extramarital affairs   b. people who hold more
    permissive values toward premarital sex also hold more per-
    missive values toward extramarital sex   c. people who

hold more permissive attitudes toward premarital sex are
more likely to become engaged in extramarital affairs
*d. all of the above

34. Lonnie Myers, in her discussion of compartment four, has
    argued that   (pp. 459-460)
    a. extramarital affairs are wrong   b. extramarital affairs
    are O.K. if both partners know about the affairs
    *c. extramarital affairs are O.K. if they are part of a
    spouse's allotted private time   d. extramarital affairs
    are O.K. if two or more couples are involved and all agree
    to take part

35. Walster and her colleagues' explanation for husbands' per-
    ceptions of extramarital sex as more destructive than wives'
    perceptions is that   (p. 461)
    a. there is a double standard that gives men more freedom
    b. men harbor greater feelings of jealousy than women
    c. men are more directed toward sexual variety than females
    *d. males are benefitted more by the marriage than females
    and are thus hurt more if the marriage breaks up

36. Which of the following types of open marriage is most
    demanding?   (p. 462)
    a. swinging   b. mate-exchange   *c. group marriage
    d. all of these forms of open marriage are equally demanding

37. Gimartin, in a series of studies, has found that, compared
    to non-swingers, swingers   (p. 462)
    *a. have less satisfying relationships with their parents
    b. have less happier personal lives and marriages
    c. are more likely to have been in therapy   d. all of the
    above

38. People are more likely to get divorced if   (p. 471)
    a. they wait until their twenties to marry   *b. they have
    been divorced once before   c. they complete their
    education   d. both b and c   e. all of the above

39. Following divorce   (p. 471)
    a. women are more likely to commit suicide than men
    b. men become less sexually active   *c. women who hold
    more egalitarian views find it easier to adjust than those
    with sex-typed expectations   d. women become less sexually
    active

40. According to Erikson, the middle life crisis involves
    (p. 472)
    a. trust and mistrust   *b. generativity vs stagnation
    c. industry vs inferiority   d. intimacy vs isolation

41. The climacteric refers to (p. 473)
    a. the tension involved following a separation or divorce
    b. the depressing period following the initial phase of a
    love affair   *c. the biological changes that occur as
    a person moves from the fertile to the nonfertile phase of
    his or her life   d. the exciting changes involved in
    an extramarital affair

42. Midlife difficulties are generally less for (p. 474)
    a. males with strong masculine images   b. females with
    strong feminine images   *c. males and females who are
    flexible in their gender role identification
    d. both a and b

43. According to Erikson, the last stage of life contains the
    challenge of (p. 474)
    a. generativity vs stagnation   *b. integrity vs despair
    c. industry vs inferiority   d. autonomy vs doubt

44. In males, Kinsey found this factor affected frequency of
    sexual outlet more than any other factor (p. 478)
    a. whether or not they held egalitarian views about sex
    b. marital happiness   c. religious values   *d. age

45. Due to cultural and social restrictions on females, Kinsey
    and his colleagues felt that the best index of female sex-
    uality for research purposes was (p. 479)
    *a. frequency of masturbation   b. frequency of intercourse
    c. frequency of orgasm   d. frequency of sexual contact
    of any kind

46. Large decreases in sexual activity from ages 45 to 70 have
    been found using (p. 480)
    a. crossectional and longitudinal research   *b. crossec-
    tional, but not longitudinal research   c. longitudinal,
    but not crossectional research   d. none of the above;
    no decreases have been found

47. Among the elderly, greater capacity for sexual interaction
    is associated with (p. 480)
    a. more past sexual activity   b. greater opportunity
    c. more children   *d. both a and b   e. all of the
    above

48. Which of the following physiological changes occur in males
    as they age? (pp. 475-476)
    *a. the secretion of androgen declines   b. the ability
    to have orgasm is lost   c. penile erections can be
    maintained only for a short period of time   d. both a and b
    e. all of the above

49. Which of the following physiological changes occur in females as they age? (p. 476)
a. the secretion of estrogen   b. intercourse is more pain-ful   c. the vagina, uterus, and cervix become smaller
d. both a and b   *e. all of the above

50. Adults are perceived by their children as_____than a normative sample of adults. (p. 477)
a. being more sexually active   b. having more extramarital affairs   *c. being more happily married   d. all of the above

51. Studies of the effect of retirement on marriage have focused on (p. 481)
*a. gender role differentiation   b. the ability to enjoy sexual interaction   c. the frequency of sexual interaction
d. all of the above

52. Which of the following statements about widowhood is correct? (p. 482)
a. there are more widowed men than widowed women   b. women experience greater trauma than men when marriages terminate due to death   *c. older unmarried women are becoming more open to masturbation as a sexual outlet   d. widowed men have greater difficulty finding a sexual partner than widowed women

53. Research on institutionalization of the aged indicates (p. 482)
*a. many nursing home residents retain sexual interests and activity   b. many residents and staff are quite knowledge-able about sexuality   c. most Americans beyond 65 are confined to nursing homes and institutions
d. institutional design and planning is specially geared to the sexual needs of the elderly

54. Silverstone and Wynter introduced a heterosexual living arrangement in a nursing home and found (p. 482)
a. increased sexual contact   b. improved self-care
c. a more cheerful atmosphere   d. both a and c
*e. all of the above

55. Research indicates that greater sexual activity is associated with (p. 483)
a. reduced insomnia   b. the relief of pain from arthritis
c. less depression   *d. all of the above

TRUE-FALSE QUESTIONS

A single underscore indicates the correct answer.

T F 1. There appears to be a strong link between prostitution and economic factors. (p. 464

T F 2. The legality of undercover operations to obtain arrests for prostitution is being challenged in the courts. (p. 466)

T F 3. Many city and state governments have had a surprising amount of success controlling prostitution. (p. 466)

T F 4. The nature of prostitution has changed quite markedly in the twentieth century. (p. 467)

T F 5. Over two-thirds of Kinsey's sample of white males had had some experience with prostitutes. (p. 470)

T F 6. Hunt's data indicate the use of prostitutes by men under 35 is increasing. (p. 470)

T F 7. Sexuality has been treated in this culture as a quality and an activity limited to the young. (p. 452)

T F 8. As we grow older, we become more alike in our sexual attitudes and behaviors. (p. 453)

T F 9 The median age of people in the U.S. is increasing. (p. 453)

T F 10. For many nonhuman species, reproductive potential continues until death. (p. 454)

T F 11. Few couples who seldom have intercourse or sexual encounters report happy marriages. (p. 455)

T F 12. The importance of sexual satisfaction in marital happiness appears to decline with the length of the marriage. (p. 455)

T F 13. Affection and loyalty are relatively more important than sexual intimacy in the second half of life for married couples. (p. 456)

T F 14. Sexual monotony is cited as a reason for marital failure more frequently by females than by males. (p. 457)

T F 15. Middle aged married women's health is better and they live longer than do single women, while the opposite is true for married men as opposed to single men. (p. 457)

166

T F 16. Husbands are more likely to be involved in extramarital affairs than are wives. (p. 458)

T F 17. The authors of the book agree with the viewpoint that extramarital affairs are evidence of a lack of morality and maturity of those participating. (p. 470)

T F 18. The key conflict behind Lonnie Myers defense of extra-marital affairs is openness. (pp. 459-460)

T F 19. Gilmartin found that swingers were more likely to have been through a divorce than non-swingers. (p. 462)

T F 20 In general, swingers are much more liberal than non-swingers in their political ideologies. (p. 463)

T F 21. The climacteric is more readily apparent in women than in men. (p. 473)

T F 22. Sexual activity among older people usually changes, and thus, is quite different from patterns established when the people were younger. (p. 477)

T F 23. The rate at which females masturbate decreases steadily with age. (p. 479)

T F 24. The rate at which males orgasm decreases steadily with age. (p. 476)

T F 25. The effects of aging on sexuality are more obvious and dramatic in the male than in the female. (p. 478)

T F 26. Most children perceive their parents as more erotic than would be expected of a normative sample of adults. (p. 477)

T F 27. Studies of the effects of retirement show that the hus-band shifts from his role of provider for the more expressive role of helping take care of household chores. (p. 481)

T F 28. Women are less likely than men to have people other than their spouse with whom they feel close or intimate. (pp. 480-481)

T F 29. The authors of this book believe that sexual feelings and expressions of the elderly should be nurtured rather than suppressed. (p. 484)

T F 30. Research indicates that increased sexual activity on the part of the elderly is associated with better health. (p. 483)

CHAPTER 17

SEXUAL PREFERENCE

MULTIPLE-CHOICE QUESTIONS

An asterisk to the left of the item indicates the correct
answer.

1. Most gays (p. 487)
    a. are swishy or effeminate   b. are simultaneously
    involved in relationships with women   c. have a tendency
    toward transvestism   *d. none of the above

2. In classifying sexual preference Kinsey emphasized (p. 488)
    a. biological factors   b. early childhood influences
    *c. behavioral criteria   d. fantasy

3. To measure sexual preference Kinsey used a   (p. 487)
    a. two point scale--heterosexual, homosexual
    b. three point scale--heterosexual, homosexual, bisexual
    *c. a seven point scale ranging from exclusively homosexual
    to exclusively heterosexual   d. a nine point Likert scale

4. Most scientists focus on_____to classify individual's
    sexual preferences. (p. 489)
    a. hormones   b. behavior   c. self-definition
    *d. both b and c   e. all of the above

5. Among adult female rhesus monkeys, the mounters are usually
    in the_____stage of the estrus cycle and the mountee is
    in the_____stage. (p. 489)
    *a. preovulatory, ovulatory   b. ovulatory, postovulatory
    c. postovulatory, preovulatory   d. ovulatory, ovulatory

6. Male-male mountings are more likely to occur when (p. 489)
    a. both males display "masculine" behavior   b. both males
    display "feminine" behavior   *c. one male displays
    "masculine" behavior and the other displays "feminine" behav-
    ior   d. none of the above; mounting behavior does not
    depend on the "masculine" or "feminine" behavior of the
    participants

7. Frank Beach has relied on the principle of_____in exploring
    connections between homosexual behavior in humans and other
    species. (p. 489)
    a. least effort   b. catharthis   c. ethrocentrism
    *d. S-R complementarity

8. According to the authors of the text, the assertion that
    homosexuality is "biologically normal" (p. 490)
    a. is supported by empirical evidence   b. is refuted by

168

empirical evidence   c. is a philosophical question
*d. is not supported or refuted by empirical evidence

9. The information about homosexual expression in other cultures
    is primarily based on the observations of (p. 490)
    *a. anthropologists   b. sociologists
    c. psychologists   d. historians

10. Homosexuality among young females is common in the culture(s)
    of (pp. 490-491)
    a. the KuKuKuKu   b. the Bataak people of the island
    of Sumatra   c. Melanesian people living on an island in
    the Pacific   *d. none of the above   e. all of the above

11. In Lebanese culture, male couples holding hands are most
    likely   (p. 491)
    *a. just friends   b. homosexuals   c. married
    d. relatives

12. Which of the following statements concerning homosexual sexual
    interaction is supported by research in England and the United
    States? (p. 492)
    a. most homosexual men are attracted to feminine partners
    b. most lesbians are attracted to masculine partners
    *c. a substantial portion of male homosexuals express both
    masculine and feminine roles   d. all of the above

13. There is no stigma atttached to the active (inserter) partici-
    pation in homosexual encounters in   (p. 492)
    a. middle and upper class America   *b. Brazil
    c. middle and upper class England   d. all of the above

14. In which of the following countries are gender role stereo-
    types most rigid? (p. 492)
    a. England   b. America   *c. Mexico   d. Denmark

15. Most homosexuals have been prosecuted under (p. 493)
    a. pornography laws   *b. sodomy laws
    c. homosexuality laws   d. fornication laws

16. The Supreme Court ruled that (p. 493)
    a. private homosexual acts are illegal   b. sodomy laws were
    unconstitutional   *c. decriminalization of sodomy laws is
    an issue to be decided by state legislatures   d. homo-
    sexuality is a moral not a legal issue

17. According to federal and state laws, discrimination against
    homosexuals in which of the following areas is illegal?
    (p. 493)
    a. housing   b. employment   c. marriage
    *d. none of the above   e. all of the above

18. Beach uses the concept of_____to explain the more frequent occurrence of heterosexual than of homosexual behavior among animals (p. 490)
    *a. sex-linked prepotency   b. S-R complementority
    c. both a and b   e. neither a nor b

19. Male homosexual sexual activity (p. 496)
    *a. is more frequent than lesbian sexual activity
    b. are more frequent in middle age years than in teenage years
    c. often lead to an exclusively homosexual lifestyle
    d. both a and b   e. all of the above

20. Female homosexual activity (p. 496)
    a. is more frequent than male homosexual sexual activity
    *b. is more frequent in the middle ages than in adolescence
    c. often lead to an exclusively homosexual lifestyle
    d. both a and b   e. all of the above

21. Research on gay males indicate that (p. 497)
    a. the acquisition of a gay identity is a sudden process
    b. most engage in a homosexual love relationship shortly
    after they realize they are gay   *c. they identify
    themselves at an early age in a supportive environment
    d. all of the above

22. Which of the following statements concerning gay lifestyles
    is correct? (pp. 497-498)
    a. the lowest incidence of cruising occurs in public rest-
    rooms and movie theatres   b. homosexuals search for
    most of the same things that heterosexuals do
    c. almost all gay males and females have been involved in a
    relatively steady relationship with a same-gender person
    during part of their life   *d. all of the above

23. Concerning the application of sexual stimulation, Masters
    and Johnson found that gay people are more_____than
    heterosexuals. (p. 499)
    a. performance oriented   b. demanding   *c. communicative
    d. both a and b

24. Female homosexuals frequently engage in (p. 499)
    *a. tribadism   b. interfemoral intercourse
    c. analingus   d. all of the above

25. Peplau and her colleagues found that heterosexuals_____
    than homosexuals in relationships. (p. 501)
    a. were more committed   b. were more satisfied
    *c. gave more importance to sexual exclusivity
    d. were more romantic

26. Gender differences that have been found among homosexuals
    include (p. 501)   a. lesbian love affairs are longer

170

lasting than male homosexual love affairs   b. public
cruising is much less frequent among lesbians than among male
homosexuals   c. lesbians have fewer sexual partners
than male homosexuals   *d. all of the above

27. _____has argued that lesbian and gay male sexual behavior
represents a pure form of male and female sexuality (p. 501)
a. Masters and Johnson   *b. Symons   c. Bell and
Weinberg   d. Peplau

28. Which of the following statements is best supported by research? (p. 502)
a. as opposed by heterosexuals, among gays, younger gays
tend to have better self-concepts than older gays
*b. in general, homosexuals experience the same general
age-related changes as do their heterosexual counterparts
c. homosexuals do not experience a mid-life crisis to the
same degree that heterosexuals do   d. most sexual
offenses committed against children involve homosexual males

29. Most of the people who engage in same-gender relations in
prison (p. 503)
a. were homosexuals before they entered prison   b. con-
tinue same gender relations after leaving prison
c. both a and b   *d. neither a nor b

30. Flaws in Kallman's research on the influence of heredity on
sexual preference include (p. 504)
*a. criteria for determining sexual preference were not
specified   b. there was no control group   c. the
findings were not statistically significant   d. both a and
b   e. all of the above

31. Research on androgens indicates they affect (p. 505)
a. sexual preference in males or females with hypogonal
conditions   b. sexual preference only if decreased
through surgical castration or chemical means
c. sexual perference in males but not females   *d. sexual
interest but not sexual preference in both males and females

32. Findings from endocrine research on homosexuals are difficult
to interpret because (p. 505)
a. nonrepresentative samples   b. failure to specify
criteria for sexual preference   *c. hormone levels can
fluctuate widely in a 24-hour period   d. all of the
above

33. Bieber's (1962) theory concerning the triangular system in
the family has been questioned becuase (p. 506)
a. his results are based only on people in therapy
b. many homosexuals did not come from the triangular family

171

system   c. many heterosexuals did come from the tri-angular family system   *d. all of the above

34. The link between gender nonconformity and homosexuality is clouded because (p. 507)
*a. of the manner in which information was obtained
b. results are based only on people in therapy   c. the un-reliability of response measures   d. criteria for specifying sexual preference were not given

35. A commonality of hereditary, hormone, and harmful family pattern theories is that (pp. 507-508)
a. they explain both homosexuality and heterosexuality
*b. they assume that attraction to same gender people results from some pathological condition   c. they are all well-supported by research   d. none of the above

36. Storms   (1980, 1981) maintains that the development of sexual identity is closely linked to (p. 508)
a. family patterns   b. hormones   *c. the development of erotic fantasies   d. nonconforming gender roles during childhood

37. According to Storms, which of the following circumstances should be more likely to lead to homosexuality? (p. 508)
a. early sexual maturation   b. prolonged experiences with same gender peers beyond puberty   c. unhappy relation-ship among peers   *d. both a and b   e. all of the above

38. A problem with many earlier studies on the adjustment of homo-sexuals is that (p. 509)
a. the experimenter was involved with subjects outside of the experiment   b. homosexuals used in research were in therapy
c. control groups of heterosexuals were not in therapy
*d. both b and c   e. all of the above

39. Chesler's theory on the adjustment of homosexuals emphasizes _____ factors. (p. 510)
a. hormonal   b. psychological   c. maturational
*d. cultural

40. Which of the following statements concerning therapy for changing sexual preference is correct? (pp. 511-512)
a. the use of therapy for this purpose is on the rise
b. psychoanalysis and behavior therapy have been very effec-tive   *c. these theories assume that sexual preference is pathological   d. all of the above

41. Compared to people who are tolerant of others' sexual prefer-ence those people who are very anti-homosexual (pp. 512-513)
*a. view sex as primarily for procreation purposes   b. are from urban areas   c. seldom attend church   d. none of the above

172

42. The theory that homophobia works to reaffirm one's own normalcy has been proposed by   (p. 513)
    a. Kinsey   *b. Szasz   c. Masters and Johnson
    d. Rafferty

43. Blumstein and Schwartz (1978) found which of the following themes among bisexuals   (p. 515)
    a. close emotional friendship that eventually evolved to sexual involvement   b. interaction in group sex
    c. belief systems that bisexuality was a natural state
    *d. all of the above

TRUE-FALSE QUESTIONS

A single underscore indicates the correct answer.

T F 1. Most research has focused on heterosexual rather than same gender sexual preference. (p. 486)

T F 2. Gender role identities of gay men and lesbians are generally consistent with their sexual preference. (p.487)

T F 3. Kinsey found that more than one in three males have had a homosexual encounter. (p. 487)

T F 4. Kinsey measured homosexuality on a continuous scale. (p. 487)

T F 5. Homosexual behavior is common among various nonhuman mammals. (p. 489)

T F 6. The principle of sex-linked prepotency states that the female stimulus pattern is correlated with the execution of masculine coital responses and vice versa. (p. 489)

T F 7. Homosexual behavior among nonhuman mammals is associated with deficiencies and excesses of hormones appropriate for the animal's gender. (p. 489)

T F 8. Clellan Ford and Frank Beach (1951) found that in the majority of cultures in which homosexuality was referenced, same-gender relations were considered to be normal and socially acceptable for certain members of the community. (p. 490)

T F 9. Most evidence supports the popular assumption that "inappropriate" gender role identification predisposes people to engage in homosexual behavior. (p. 492)

T F 10. In Brazil only the insertee in male homosexual relationships is considered to be a homosexual. (p. 492)

T _F_ 11. Homosexuality is currently classified as a mental illness. (p. 493)

_T_ F 12. Research over the past three decades has failed to establish any direct connection between homosexual preference and mental or emotional disorders. (p. 493)

_T_ F 13. The legal climate has been improving in North America for homosexuals. (p. 493)

T _F_ 14. Homosexuals can be denied entrance to the U.S. under the McCarran Act. (p. 493)

_T_ F 15. Many people in our culture reserve the label "heterosexual" for people who have only had sexual interaction with members of the other gender. (p. 487)

T _F_ 16. About 50% of males who have had a homosexual experience during their teenage years become exclusively homosexual. (p. 496)

T _F_ 17. We find it more difficult to use dichotomies to describe others than to describe ourselves. (p. 496)

_T_ F 18. The acquisition of a gay identity is a gradual process. (p. 497)

T _F_ 19. Most male homosexuals have engaged in homosexual love relationships by age 20. (p. 497)

T _F_ 20. Most homosexuals are open about their homosexuality. (p. 497)

_T_ F 21. Methods of sexual expression for homosexuals and heterosexuals in foreplay and lovemaking are very similar. (p. 499)

T _F_ 22. Masters and Johnson's findings concerning homosexuals' sexual expression have been well supported by other researchers. (pp. 499-500)

_T_ F 23. Masters and Johnson found no differences in the pattern of sexual arousal and orgasm in heterosexuals and homosexuals. (p. 499)

T _F_ 24. Most research on homosexual expression has focused on fantasies and feelings. (p. 500)

_T_ F 25. Venereal disease has been much more frequently reported among male homosexuals than among lesbians. (p. 501)

T F 26. Most studies suggest that homosexuals experience the same general age-related changes as do their hetero-sexual counterparts. (p. 502)

T F 27. Homosexual relations are faily common in the military despite the grave risks. (p. 503)

T F 28. Most theorizing about the influence of heredity on homosexuality has viewed homosexuality as very adaptive from an evolutionary perspective. (p. 504)

T F 29. There is little support for hormonal explanations of sexuality at the present time. (p. 505)

T F 30. Available research indicates that disturbed parental relations are probably very important for the develop-ment of homosexuality. (pp. 506-507)

T F 31. Recent reviews of studies indicate that there is little evidence to support the view that there are differences in adjustment between homosexuals and heterosexuals. (p. 511)

T F 32. Little research has been obtained on bisexuals. (p.516)

CHAPTER 18

DISEASES AND DISABILITIES

MULTIPLE-CHOICE QUESTIONS

An asterisk to the left of the item indicates the correct answer.

1. Today, the most common infection reported to public health authorities is (p. 519)
a. syphilis   b. herpes simplex Type 2
*c. gonorrhea   d. nongonacoccal urethritis

2. Which of the following statements correctly reflects the knowledge of college students concerning STD's? (p. 522)
*a. college students are not well informed about the facts regarding STDs   b. the more knowledgeable students tend to be more confident about the accuracy of their informa-tion   c. most college students learn about STDs from their parents   d. both a and b

3. Which of the following infections is relatively easy to cure? (p. 522)
*a. gonorrhea   b. herpes simplex Type 2
c. genital warts   d. hepatitis B

4. Darrow's major point concerning STD's is (p. 523)
   a. the failure to educate youngsters in schools can only lead
   to a higher incidence of STD's   b. more money must be
   made available to study the causes of STD's
   *c. physicians have been negligent in their efforts to control
   STD's   d. abstinence is the best method for preventing
   STD's

5. Gonorrhea is (p. 524)
   *a. asymptomatic in most women   b. asymptomatic in most
   men   c. more common among men and women over 25
   d. caused by a virus   e. all of the above

6. Gonorrhea is usually treated with (p. 525)
   a. tetracycline   b. sulfisoxazale   *c. penicillin
   d. streptomycin

7. PPNG is (p. 525)
   a. used to treat gonorrhea   b. used to treat syphillis
   *c. a penicillin resistant strain of gonorrhea
   d. a pencillin resistant strain of nongonococcal urethritis

8. The most likely cause of acute PID is (p. 526)
   a. syphillis   *b. gonorrhea   c. Herpes Simplex II
   d. nongonoccocal urethritis

9. Untreated gonorrhea can lead to (p. 526)
   a. infertility   b. ectopic pregnancy   c. acute PID
   *d. all of the above

10. Which of the following reduces the risk of contracting an
    STD? (p. 536)
    a. taking showers or baths before being sexually intimate
    b. urinating before sex   c. using condoms during inter-
    course   *d. both a and c   e. all of the above

11. Symptoms of this STD include a thin, relatively clear,
    whitish discharge from the urethra (p. 537)
    a. gonorrhea   *b. NGU   c. syphillis   d. Herpes Simplex
    II

12. The most common infection of the urethra seen among white
    affluent American males is (p. 527)
    a. gonorrhea   *b. NGU   c. syphillis   d. Herpes Simplex II

13. Which of the following STD's is found only in men? (p. 535)
    a. NGU   b. Herpes Simplex II   *c. prostatitis
    d. none of the above

14. NGU is often treated with (p. 527)
    *a. tetracycline   b. sulfisoxazale   c. penicillin
    d. streptomycin

15. Which of the following STD's is transmitted only through intercourse (p. 532)
a. gonorrhea   b. syphillis   *c. genital warts
d. none of the above

16. Which of the following STD's has been increasing in incidence. (p. 519)
a. gonorrhea   b. syphillis   c. NGU   *d. all of the above

17. This STD is transmitted through contact with hard but painless sores called chancres   (p. 528)
a. gonorrhea   *b. syphillis   c. NGU   d. Herpes Simplex II

18. This STD is transmitted through oral stimulation of the anus and is diagnosed through culturing a stool specimen.   (p.531)
a. chancroid   b. granuloma inguinale
*c. shigellosis   d. candidiasis

19. Of the following infections, which is most difficult to cure? (p. 531)
a. gonorrhea   b. syphilis   c. NGU   *d. Herpes Simplex II

20. The growth of this virus can be reduced by an ointment (Zovirax)   (p. 531)
*a. Herpes Simplex II   b. Hepititis B   c. genital warts
d. all of the above

21. This STD is linked to cancer and can maim or kill the off-spring of women afflicted with it.   (p. 531)
a. Herpes Simplex I   *b. Herpes Simplex II
c. gonorrhea   d. Hepatitis B

22. This STD is diagnosed through visual inspection (p. 532)
a. gonorrhea   b. syphillis   *c. genital warts
d. vaginitis

23. Which of the following statements concerning trichomoniasis is correct? (p. 533)
a. it is diagnosed through visual inspection   *b. most people who have it are asymptomatic   c. it has severe consequences for the fetus if active in women during labor
d. both b and c   e. all of the above

24. Cystitis (pp. 534-535)
a. is very painful   b. is more common among women
c. can result from wiping from the anus toward the urethra
d. both b and c   *e. all of the above

25. The STD, pediculosis pubis, better known as crabs, is a_____
infection. (p. 536)   a. bacterial   b. viral   c. vaginal
*d. parasitic

26. Surgical removal of a cancerous breast is called   (p. 539)
    *a. mastectomy   b. vasectomy   c. hysterectomy
    d. appendectomy

27. Which of the following statements about breast cancer in
    women is true?   (p. 539)
    a. in most cases it is self-diagnosed   b. most women
    examine their breasts monthly to check for cancer
    c. publication of the fact that most breast lumps are non-
    malignant increases the likelihood that women will examine
    themselves   *d. both a and c   e. all of the above

28. Which of the following treatments is recommended for breast
    cancer by the American Cancer Society? (p. 539)
    a. modified mastectomy   *b. radical mastectomy
    c. lumpectomy   d. both b and c   e. all of the above

29. Breast cancer is associated with   (p. 537)
    a. late menstruators   b. early menopause,
    *c. postponed first childbirth   d. both a and b
    e. all of the above

30. A method of breast cancer detection that avoids exposure to
    x-rays is   (p. 539)
    a. mammography   b. xeroradiography   *c. thermography
    d. none of the above

31. Cope argues against routine use of radical mastectomy and
    favors lumpectomy instead because radical mastectomy (p. 539)
    *a. is more painful   b. lumpectomy removes more of the
    cancerous tissue   c. both a and b   d. none of the
    above; Cope argues in favor of routine use of radical mastec-
    tomy

32. Few women have undergone the procedure of breast reconstruc-
    tion because   (p. 539)
    a. it is expensive   b. the surgery tends to produce exten-
    sive scarring   c. the implanted breast often does not
    look natural   *d. all of the above

33. According to Witkin, a major factor influencing a woman's
    recovery from a mastectomy is   (p. 538)   a. the type of surg-
    ery--radical mastectomy vs. modified mastectomy
    b. the type of drugs administered after surgery
    *c. the reaction of her husband or lover   d. the amount
    of physical pain endured

34. Cervical cancer occurs more frequently in women who (p. 541)
    a. began sexual intercourse at an early age   b. have a
    large number of sexual partners   c. who were prenatally
    exposed to DES   d. both b and c   *e. all of the above

178

35. In which of the following stages is arousal likely to be re-
    duced in women who have had a hysterectomy   (p. 542)
    a. excitement   b. plateau   c. orgasm   d. resolution
    *d. all of the above

36. Estrogen replacement therapy for ovariectomized women is
    controversial because   (p. 543)
    a. it leads to less lubrication   *b. estrogen might be
    linked to cancer   c. it increases susceptibility to STD's
    d. it is associated with various side effects such as nausea,
    hair loss

37. Prostate cancer   (p. 543)
    *a. is rare for males under 50   b. has a high mortality
    rate for men over 50   c. is associated with infrequent
    urination   d. is usually treated with androgen

38. Testicular cancer   (p. 544)
    a. is rare for males under 50   *b. can be detected by
    self-examination   c. is associated with infrequent urina-
    tion   d. is usually treated with androgen

39. Which of the following cancers has recently begun to appear
    in connection with acquired immune deficiency syndrome (AIDS)
    among young and middle aged gay males.   (p. 545)
    a. prostate cancer   *b. Karposi's Sarcoma
    c. testular cancer   d. breast cancer

40. Within two years of developing AIDs symptoms about_____of
    those afflicted have died.   (p. 545)
    a. 10%   b. 33%   c. 50%   *d. 70%

41. Diabetes mellitus in men   (p. 546)
    *a. is often associated with erectile dysfunction
    b. is often associated with prostate cancer   c. is usually
    treated with androgen   d. all of the above

TRUE-FALSE QUESTIONS

    A single underscore indicates the correct answer.

T F 1. Twenty-five years ago, the incidence of sexually trans-
          mitted disease was at a record low.   (p. 519)

T F 2. People who are sexually active should obtain periodic
          lab tests for the presence of STD's even in the absence
          of recognizable symptoms

T F 3. Even people engaging in sexual intimacy with only one
          person can easily become infected.

T F 4. Women who use the IUD are more likely to develop PID
          than non-users of the IUD   (p. 526)

T F 5. Gonorrhea is diagnosed through examination of a blood sample under a microscope. (p. 525)

T F 6. There is no vaccine currently suitable to prevent gonorrhea. (p. 525)

T F 7. NGU is generally a more serious disease than gonorrhea for men. (p. 527)

T F 8. The highest incidence of syphillis occurs in people over 25. (p. 528)

T F 9. The probability of infection from one contact with a syphillis carrier is very small. (p. 528)

T F 10. For most STD's, natural immunities develop making it extremely unlikely to become reinfected. (p. 529)

T F 11. Only a few people with untreated syphilis reach the final and potentially deadly last stage. (p. 529)

T F 12. STD's can only be transmitted by sexual contact. (p.522)

T F 13. STD's caused by bacteria are easier to treat than STD's caused by viruses. (p. 524)

T F 14. In its dormant phase, Herpes 2 is not contagious. (p. 531)

T F 15. If Herpes 2 is active when a women is in labor, then the baby should be delivered cesarean section. (p. 531)

T F 16. Vaginal infections are associated with irritating itches rather than very painful burning sensations. (p. 533)

T F 17. Cancer of the prostate gland in men is one of the most common forms of cancer in adults. (p. 543)

T F 18. Breast cancer is very common among men as well as women. (p. 537)

T F 19. Marijuana can be used with cancer patients to reduce nausea resulting from chemotherapy. (p. 537)

T F 20. Breast cancer is higher among women who take the pill. (p. 537)

T F 21. Breast cancer is rare among women under 25. (p. 537)

T F 22. The Pap test is a screening procedure for breast cancer. (p. 542)

T F 23. Today, the emphasis in most explanations of variations in sexual behavior is on social rather than biological factors. (p. 542)

T F 24. Hysterectomies have no effect on sexual expression in most women. (p. 542)

T F 25. Women who have their ovaries removed have the hormonal and sexual characteristics of aging women. (p. 543)

T F 26. Most men over 60 develop enlarged prostate glands. (p. 543)

T F 27. In most cases, vascular illnesses do not impose a permanent ban on sexual interaction. (p. 545)

T F 28. Spinal-cord injured women are unable to conceive and give birth. (p. 546)

CHAPTER 19

COERCIVE SEXUAL BEHAVIOR

MULTIPLE-CHOICE QUESTIONS

An asterisk to the left of the item indicates the correct answer.

1. The connecting thread among sexual behaviors such as rape, sexual harassment, and incest is (p. 550)
a. deviancy   b. aggression   *c. coercion   d. physical abuse

2. Johnson estimates that women just entering adolescence at this time have a_____chance of being the victim of sexual assault at some point in their life.   (p.551)
a. 1%   b. 10-20%   *c. 20-30%   d. greater than 50%

3. The McCahill study was less biased than other studies in that (p. 551)
a. research was conducted on victims who did not report the assault   b. research was conducted on offenders who had not been convicted   *c. research was conducted on victims who had just recently been assaulted
d. all of the above

4. Women in which of the following age groups are at the greatest risk of sexual assault? (p. 554)
a. 11-14 years   b. 15-19 years   *c. 20-24 years
d. 25-29 years

5. The most often cited reason for reporting rape in the McCahill study was (p. 554)
    *a. desire for help   b. to punish rapists   c. concern
    for future victims   d. feeling of social responsibility

6. Women who are assaulted by men they are dating will usually report it to (p. 555)
    a. their family   b. legal authorities   c. counselors
    *d. none of the above; such assaults are seldom reported

7. In one study by Parcell and Kanin (1976), it was found that resistance to sexual aggression was most often characterized by (p. 555)
    *a. arguing or fighting   b. pleading   c. screaming or
    crying   d. running away

8. In the Parcell and Kanin (1976) study the prevailing emotion following sexual aggression was (p. 555)
    *a. hostility   b. fear   c. guilt   d. emotional hurt

9. Which of the following statements is most accurate concerning gang assault? (p. 556)
    *a. advance planning is more likely than in incidents with a
    single assailant   b. the group committing the act
    usually knows the victim   c. the most common form of
    gang rape involes two or three men usually in their mid to
    late twenties   d. only about 10% of all rapes involve
    more than one assailant

10. Compared to female victims of sexual assault, male victims of sexual assault (p. 557)
    a. were more reluctant to reveal initially the fact that rape
    had occurred   b. sustained more physical trauma
    c. were more likely to have been assaulted by multiple
    assailants   *d. all of the above

11. Which of the following tactics is most common among rape episodes involving male victims? (p. 557)
    a. entrapment   b. deception   *c. physical force
    d. nonaggressive persuasion

12. Most male rapists are in the age group (p. 558)
    a. 15-19   *b. 20-24   c. 25-29   d. 30-34

13. In the majority of rapes (p. 558)
    a. a weapon is involved   b. the offender is drinking
    c. physical force is used   d. both b and c
    *e. all of the above

14. Convicted sex offenders (p. 558)   a. tend to lack self-
    confidence   b. are more likely to have been victims of vio-
    lent sexual abuse   c. often report a pattern of sexually

182

victimizing others during childhood and adolescence
*d. all of the above

15. Most rapists have been found to (p. 559)
a. have high sex drives   b. have very low IQ
c. be very selective in choosing their victims
*d. none of the above

16. A national survey sponsored by the Federal Commission on
Crimes of Violence concluded that about____of rape charges
involve victim precipitation. (p. 560)
*a. 5%   b. 15%   c. 25%   d. 50%

17. Which of the following statements is false? (p. 561)
a. most people believe that rape is a sex crime   b. most
people believe that rape is committed by sexually frustrated
individuals   *c. evidence indicates that prostitution
appears to reduce the incidence of rape   d. none of the
above

18. Which of the following statements concerning the importance
of gender roles in contributing to sexual assault is correct?
*a. many rapists believe that their victims actually enjoyed
the sexual prowess of the assailant
b. women are encouraged to be easy prey for men   c. the traditional man is led to believe that women are very interested
in sex   d. greater role rigidity in cultures is correlated with lower levels of violence

19. Feild and Bienen (1980) found that people who view women in
traditional roles are (p. 563)
a. likely to see rape as being the man's fault   b. likely
to see rape as being motivated by aggression rather than sex
*c. in favor of harsh sentences for rapists   d. none of
the above

20. The research of Neil Malamuth and his colleagues has focused
on (p. 563)
a. rapists vs nonrapists views on sexuality   *b. force-
oriented vs non-force-oriented volunteers   c. gender role
rigidity   d. the aftermath of sexual assaults

21. Force-oriented individuals (p. 564)
*a. are more aroused by rape than non-force-oriented indivi-
duals   b. are more aroused by mutually consenting
sexual partners than non-force-oriented individuals
c. both a and b   d. neither a nor b

22. Which of the following is the last phase of Burgess and
Holmstrom's (1974) rape trauma syndrome? (p. 567)
a. the acute phase   *b. the reorganization phase
c. the expressive reaction phase   d. the controlled
reaction phase

23. Immediately after an assault, the victim should first (p.569)
    a. call the police   *b. call a rape crisis center
    c. call her boyfriend or parents   d. pretend it didn't
    happen

24. Which of the following reasons often given by police, is a
    legitimate one for declaring an assault charge unfounded?
    (p. 569)
    a. if it is believed the victim "asked for it"   *b. obvious
    discrepancies in the victim's story   c. if it is believed
    that the assailant will be convicted in court   d. all of
    the above

25. Given a sexual assault charge has been declared founded, what
    are the chances a person will be convicted? (p. 570)
    a. 90%   b. 50%   c. 30%   *d. less than 10%

26. The specific definition of sexual assault is determined by
    (p. 570)
    a. the federal government   *b. the state government
    c. local governments   d. both a and c

27. The Rape Victim Privacy Act   (p. 571)
    *a. limits trial evidence of the victim's previous sexual
    experience with people other than the defendant
    b. limits trial evidence of the victim's sexual experience
    with the defendant   c. limits any information regard-
    ing the victim's personal life   d. all of the above

28. The most crucial aspect of the current definition of sexual
    assault is (p. 571)   a. whether the victim and assailant
    were strangers   b. whether the victim was threatened
    c. whether the victim was physically or psychologically
    harassed   *d. whether the victim consented

29. Which of the following statements concerning sexual harassment
    of women on the job is supported by data? (p. 572)
    a. virtuous women are seldom accosted   b. the proportion
    of cases in which the victim precipitated her own victimiza-
    tion is about 50%   *c. supervisors are more likely to
    harass subordinates than other co-workers
    d. in surveys, few American women admit to being harassed

30. Adult pedophiles   (p. 575)
    *a. are typically male   b. are usually violent
    c. usually approach strangers   d. both a and b
    e. all of the above

31. Convicted pedophiliacs tend to be   (p. 575)
    a. younger than other convicted sex offenders
    b. homosexual rather than heterosexual   c. below average
    in intelligence   *d. conservative, moralistic, and
    religious

32. The most common reaction of a child to an adult sexual overture is (p. 576)
    *a. fear   b. anger   c. disgust   d. pleasure

33. _____found that succumbing to sexual activity without physical force leads to less trauma. (p. 577)
    a. McCahill   *b. Finkelor   c. Fritz et al
    d. Florence Rush

34. As compared to adult-child sexual encounters initiated by adult males, those initiated by adult females (p. 579)
    a. were reported as more negative by the child   b. were reported as eliciting more fear by the child   *c. were reported as more interesting by the child   d. both a and b

35. Rush maintains that sexual victimization of children may be common in our society because of (p. 579)
    a. the availability of child pornography   b. the inability of the courts to confine convicted offenders
    *c. the degree of male dominance in our society   d. the degree of resentment our society holds toward such acts

36. Concerning incest Hunt (1974) found (p. 580)
    a. in most cases sexual contact was limited to light petting
    b. sexual acts were more common among better educated and white collar families   c. more than half of the reported contacts involved cousins   *d. all of the above

37. Concerning incest, Finkehor (1979) found   (pp. 580-581)
    a. relations between fathers and daughters is more common than between siblings   *b. more respondents reported sexual contact with a relative than with an unrelated older person
    c. reports of sexual contact with mothers were much more common than in the Hunt study   d. almost 50% of the incestuous relations were homosexual

38. Gebhard and his colleagues (1965) found that incest offenders (p. 581)
    *a. frequently engaged in premarital sex   b. had aggressive personalities   c. were most likely involved in homosexual encounters   d. all of the above

39. The most likely explanation for the greater incidence of father-daughter incest than mother-son incest is (pp. 581-582)
    a. women come to identify with the well-being of their children to a greater extent than do men   *b. traditionally father-initiated sexual activity was more tolerated than punished   c. there is no real difference; sexual contact by mothers is interpreted as nurturance whereas sexual contact by fathers is interpreted as incest   d. all these explanations are equally plausible

40. Which of the following conditions are associated with the risk of incest for a daughter? (p. 582)
a. an alcoholic or violent father   b. a depressed or passive mother   c. an eldest daughter who has been forced to play a "little mother" role   *d. all of the above

41. The most likely reason that the incest taboo arose many years ago was (p. 583)
a. to prevent a deterioration of genetic quality   *b. to maintain the family unit   c. any sexual contact outside marriage was considered wrong and incest was an example of such contact   d. none of the above; the incest taboo is a creation of the 20th century

TRUE-FALSE QUESTIONS

A single underscore indicates the correct answer.

T F 1. Many authorities believe the proportion of unreported sexual assaults is much greater than 50%. (p. 551)

T F 2. In the Parcell & Kanin (1976) study the pattern of assault often involved the male trying to engage in a particular sexual activity with little or no prior sex play. (p. 555)

T F 3. Parcell (1980) found that most college women appear to accept forced sexual intercourse as an expected part of male-female relationships. (p. 555)

T F 4. In most states forced sexual encounter between husband and wife is not considered sexual assault. (p. 556)

T F 5. Most of the available studies on the sexual assault of men are based on the prison environment. (p. 556)

T F 6. Few states still define rape as something a man does to a woman. (p. 557)

T F 7. It appears that those who rape males are more sexually motivated than those who rape females. (p. 557)

T F 8. Martha Burt (1980) found that a majority of adults agree that a woman who goes to the home of a man on the first date implies that she is willing to have sex. (p. 560)

T F 9. Most rapists who experienced sexual dysfunction with their victims also experience dysfunction with consenting partners. (p. 559)

T F 10. The majority of adults, both male and female, blame the victims of sexual assault for behaviors before, during, and after they have been forced to engage in sex. (p.560)

T <u>F</u> 11. Few adults believe that some women carry on sexually, then get scared and unfairly call it rape. (p. 560)

<u>T</u> F 12. In the past decade, a significant attempt has been made to reduce the trauma associated with reporting rape and with testifying in court. (p. 567)

<u>T</u> F 13. Many states have passed laws requiring counties or states to pay the cost of Medical exams at rape crisis centers. (p. 569)

T <u>F</u> 14. Over 50% of sexual assault victims report the assault to police. (p. 569)

T <u>F</u> 15. Even if a sexual assault charge is declared unfounded, it is still included in the crime statistics, and an attempt is made to locate a supposed assailant. (p.570)

T <u>F</u> 16. Gutek et al. found that women are more flattered by sexual overtures from men at work than men are. (p. 572)

<u>T</u> F 17. Sexual relations between an adult and a child are against the law in all states. (p. 574)

T <u>F</u> 18. The pattern of pedophiliac sexual activities is strikingly similar to that of exhibitionists. (p. 575)

T <u>F</u> 19. A majority of imprisoned child molesters have a primary and relatively permanent sexual interest in children. (p. 575)

T <u>F</u> 20. Most experts believe there has been an alarming increase in the frequency of pedophilia. (p. 578)

T <u>F</u> 21. Incest most frequently involves unrelated adults as participants. (p. 579)

T <u>F</u> 22. In general, the widest extension of incest taboos beyond the nuclear family is found in the most modern complex industrial societies. (p. 580)

T <u>F</u> 23. In the nuclear family the most frequently reported form of incest involves siblings. (p. 580)

T <u>F</u> 24. Research on inbreeding indicates that incest causes a deterioration of genetic quality. (p. 583)

CHAPTER 20

ATYPICAL SEXUAL ACTIVITY

MULTIPLE-CHOICE QUESTIONS

An asterisk to the left of the item indicates the correct answer.

1. The term clinicians prefer to use for behaviors such as voyeurism or exhibitionism is (p. 587)
    a. sexual deviance   *b. paraphilla   c. perversion
    d. none of the above

2. Which of the following images or acts is classified as a para-philia in DSM-III?   (p. 587)
    a. preference for the use of a nonhuman object for sexual arousal   b. repetitive sexual activity with humans in-volving real or simulated suffering or humiliation
    c. repetitive sexual activity with nonconsenting partners
    d. both a and b   *e. all of the above

3. Much of the text's information about the paraphilias comes from people (p. 587)
    a. who have been arrested   b. who are in therapy
    c. who have taken sex education classes and privately volun-teered information   *d. both a and b   e. all of the above

4. Most of our information about paraphilias comes from
    a. those who have been arrested or are in prison   b. those who are in therapy   c. females   *d. a and b
    e. none of the above

5. Which of the following is classified as a paraphilia? (pp. 588-589)
    a. transvestism   b. sexual masochism   c. exhibitionism
    *d. all of the above

6. Which of the following statements about fetishism is true? (p. 589)
    a. it is thought to be primarily a female characteristic
    b. fetishes are rarely utilized in fantasies because sexual arousal is diminished if the object is not physically present
    *c. feet, shoes and boots are commonly used as fetish objects
    d. fetishism is an activity limited to human beings

7. Historically, the foot (p. 590)
    *a. has been a male sexual symbol   b. has been a female sexual symbol   c. both a and b   d. neither a nor b

8. A fetish was regarded by Freud (1928) as (p. 591)
a. a substitute object for a vagina   *b. a substitute
object for a penis   c. an association to an object that
had been conditioned using reinforcement   d. an association to an object resulting from a genetic predisposition

9. A fetish was regarded by behaviorists as (p. 591)   a. substitute object for a vagina   b. a substitute object
for a penis   *c. an association to an object that had been
conditioned using reinforcement   d. an association to an
object resulting from a genetic predisposition

10. The most common sexual offense is (p. 591)
a. fetishism   *b. exhibitionism   c. voyeurism   d. transvestism

11. The most common reaction of the victim of an exhibitionist is
(p. 592)
a. anger   b. humor   *c. fear   d. disgust

12. Male exhibitionists (p. 592)
a. tend to get real close to their victims   *b. rarely
know their victims   c. are usually dangerous   d. none
of the above

13. Male exhibitionists (p. 593)
a. are typically in their teens the first time they expose
themselves   b. enjoy exposing themselves to older women
*c. tend to be timid and nonassertive   d. all of the above

14. Which of the following has been suggested as a plausible
cause for most cases of exhibitionism? (p. 593)
a. severe retardation   b. senility   *c. lack of assertiveness   d. impotence

15. Which of the following statements about exhibitionists is
correct? (pp. 593-594)
a. many expose themselves even when sexual contact is available in marriage   b. many are repeat offenders
c. most cases involve streaking, mooning or obscene phone calls
*d. both a and b   d. both b and c

16. It appears that the response the obscene phone caller wants
to obtain from a victim is (p. 594)
a. sexual arousal   *b. fear   c. sympathy   d. anger

17. Which of the following activities constitutes voyeurism?
(p. 595)
a. attending an X-rated movie   b. reading pornographic
magazines   c. visiting topless or bottomless bars
d. both a and c   *e. none of the above

18. Which of the following is true of voyeurs? (p. 596)
*a. those convicted are almost always male   b. many have
serious mental disorders   c. alcohol or drugs are often
involved in their peeping   d. both a and c
e. all of the above

19. Symon (1979) uses a_____perspective in explaining gender
differences in seeking sexual stimuli.   (p. 596)
a. socio-cultural   b. psychoanalytical   *c. evolutionary   d. behavioral

20. A form of sexual activity in which a couple engages in sex
while a third person looks on with the consent of the couple
is called   (p. 597)
a. buggery   b. necrophilia   *c. troilism   d. frottage

21. Which of the following is considered a paraphilia? (p. 597)
a. voyeurism   b. frottage   c. troilism   *d. both a and b
e. both a and c

22. Kinsey found a higher rate of sexual contact with animals
among (p. 598)
*a. farm boys   b. the uneducated   c. adults (as opposed
to adolescents)   d. both a and b   e. all of the above

23. The most common form of sexual interaction with animals
reported by Kinsey's male volunteers was   (p. 598)
a. hugging and kissing   *b. vaginal coitus
c. cunnilingus   d. analingus

24. Kinsey believed that individuals who have sexual contact with
animals should be (p. 598)
a. treated clinically   b. given harsh prison terms
c. both a and b   *d. neither a nor b

25. Which of the following statements concerning sadomasochistic
sexual practices is correct? (p. 599)
a. many women become sexually excited by acting sadistically
toward men   *b. sadomasochistic practices are usually
carefully scripted   c. the major theme in sadomasochistic
practices is spontaneity and give and take
d. in Western cultures, masochistic fantasies are rare in
the sexual lives of women

26. _____believed that sadism was essentially a masculine, disorder whereas masochism was a feminine disorder. (p. 601)
a. Kinsey   *b. Krafft-Ebing   c. Fromm   d. Hunt

27. The use of surgical castration as a treatment for paraphilia
    (p. 604)
    a. is based on simplistic and inaccurate reasoning
    b. has been widely practiced in some Northern European
    countries   c. has not been shown to be effective to this
    point   *d. all of the above

28. Although more research needs to be done, the most effective
    antiandrogen for inhibiting sexual response appears to be
    (p. 605)
    a. testosterone   b. estrogen   c. synthetic progestin
    *d. cyprone acetate

29. The major treatment used to decrease or eliminate inappropri-
    ate sexual arousal in North America is   (p. 606)
    a. surgical castration   *b. aversion therapy
    c. brain surgery   d. chemical castration

30. Which of the following aversion therapies is most preferred
    by therapists? (p. 606)
    a. chemical   b. olfactory   c. electrical   *d. cognitive

TRUE-FALSE QUESTIONS

    A single underscore indicates the correct answer.

T F 1. Homosexuality is considered a paraphilia in DSM-III.
          (p. 587)

T F 2. Personal or subjective considerations often play a
          greater role in labeling a person as sexually atypical
          than do objective, scientific facts. (p. 588)

T F 3. Individuals who have engaged in atypical sexual activ-
          ities, but usually do not prefer to engage in them
          are still classified as having a paraphilia. (p. 588)

T F 4. The label of fetishism is only applied when sexual
          arousal is dependent almost exclusively on the object
          of the fetish. (p. 589)

T F 5. Throughout history, the foot has been one of the most
          common phallic symbols. (p. 590)

T F 6. Public display of the genitals is against the law in
          every state. (p. 592)

T F 7. Male exhibitionists tend to have higher testosterone
          levels than normal men. (p. 593)

T F 8. The hypothesis that exhibitionism is an attempt to
          prove one's prowess is inconsistent with Freudian
          theory. (pp. 593-594)

191

T F 9. Most states have laws against voyeurism. (p. 595)

T F 10. Voyeurs often go to places where observing nude bodies is socially acceptable. (p. 595)

T F 11. Troilism is considered a sex offense. (p. 597)

T F 12. Clinically defined, zoophilia is a rare phenomenon. (p. 597)

T F 13. Kinsey concluded that around 40 to 50% of all men on farms have had some sort of sexual contact with an animal at some point in their lives. (p. 598)

T F 14. In Kinsey's study, only a few males or females reported that they experienced some type of erotic response when observing mating animals. (p. 598)

T F 15. According to DSM-III, only activities involving a non-consenting partner can be classified as sexual sadism. (p. 599)

T F 16. Many women experience sexual excitement, specifically provoked by physical pain. (p. 599)

T F 17. Research strongly supports the concept that women are inclined toward masochism and men toward sadism. (pp. 601-602)

T F 18. Public reaction to people who engage in paraphilias is often more outraged than that expressed toward rapists. (p. 603)

T F 19. Modifying paraphilias by conventional counseling or psychotherapy has not been very effective. (p. 603)

T F 20. Brain surgery to control or eliminate sexual behavior is relatively common in this country. (p. 605)

CHAPTER 21

LOVING SEXUAL INTERACTIONS

MULTIPLE-CHOICE QUESTIONS

An asterisk to the left of the item indicates the correct answer.

1. _____ has done a series of studies on the effects of early social deprivation on the development of rhesus monkeys. (pp. 609-611)   a. the Goldmans   b. Mary Calderone
   *c. Harry Harlow   d. Erik Erikson

2. Infants raised in an orphanage or institution tend to (p. 611)
    a. develop normal interpersonal relationships once they reach
    adolescence   *b. be unable to form meaningful social re-
    lationships   c. shy away from much attention and affection
    d. both a and c

3. Infant monkeys separated from their mothers spent more time
    with (p. 609)
    a. a plain wire mesh cylinder surrogate mother   b. a plain
    wire mesh cylinder surrogate mother only if it gave milk
    *c. a terry-cloth surrogate mother   d. a terry-cloth
    surrogate mother only if it gave milk

4. Monkeys isolated from their mothers for six months (p. 610)
    *a. were social misfits   b. developed abnormal reproductive
    systems   c. did not even attempt to engage in sexual
    behavior   d. both a and c   e. all of the above

5. Isolated monkeys paired with younger normal monkeys (p. 600)
    a. did not improve their interpersonal or sexual behavior
    through adulthood   b. improved their interpersonal be-
    havior, but did not develop normal sexual behavior during
    adolescence   c. did not improve their interpersonal
    behavior, but did develop normal sexual behavior during
    adolescence   *d. demonstrated improved interpersonal
    behavior and normal sexual behavior during adolescence

6. Feelings of jealousy are probably due to (p. 626)
    a. genetic factors   b. biological factors   *c. social
    factors   d. all of the above

7. In response to jealousy, (p. 627)
    *a. men, but not women, tend to seek outside relationships
    rather than make themselves more attractive to their mate
    b. women, but not men, tend to seek outside relationships
    rather than make themselves attractive to their mate
    c. both men and women tend to seek outside relationships
    rather than make themselves more attractive to their mates
    d. both men and women tend to make themselves more attractive
    to their mates rather than seek outside relationships

8. According to Miller, for a relationship to be successful, a
    delicate balance is needed between (p. 628)
    a. work and pleasure   b. emotional and sexual intimacy
    *c. sharing and privacy   d. duties performed by the hus-
    band and by the wife

9. Much research on loving care during infancy is based on (pp. 610-611)
   a. laboratory studies with children   b. laboratory studies with primates   c. observational studies of neglected children   *d. both b and c   e. all of the above

10. Infant monkeys who were separated from their mothers shortly after birth   (p. 609)
    a. grew up normally   b. were able to mate as adults
    c. both a and b   *d. neither a nor b

11. Monkeys raised in total isolation   (p. 610)
    *a. were "semi-animated vegetables"   b. were social misfits but had normal reproductive systems   c. engaged in botched sexual behavior   d. both b and c
    e. all of the above

12. Monkeys raised in partial isolation   (p. 610)
    a. were "semi-animated vegetables"   b. were social misfits but had normal reproductive systems   c. engaged in botched sexual behavior   *d. both b and c
    e. all of the above

13. The key to infants' normal development according to Harlow is (p. 611)
    a. verbal stimulation by the mother   b. constant presence of the mother   *c. contact comfort   d. all of the above

14. Observational studies of deprived, institutionalized children indicate that these children   (p. 611)
    a. are unable to form meaningful social relationships
    b. having an insatiable need for affection and attention
    *c. both a and b   d. neither a nor b

15. Prescott (1975) attributes adult aggressiveness to   (p. 611)
    a. modeling of other adults   b. unconscious sexual conflicts   *c. retarded brain development   d. all of the above

16. Maslow makes a distinction between   (p. 613)
    a. personal love; social love   b. conditional love; unconditional love   *c. deficiency love; being love
    d. self love; selfishness

17. The suggestion that apathy rather than hate is the opposite of love was made by   (p. 614)
    *a. Rollo May   b. Erich Fromm   c. Sigmund Freud
    d. Sidney Harris

18. According to Fromm, unconditional love is characterized by
    the_____ - _____ relationship (p. 614)
    a. older sibling-younger sibling   *b. mother-infant
    c. husband-wife   d. God-man

19. Most people believe that friendships between men and women
    are more difficult to establish because (p. 616)
    a. possible sexual tensions   b. there is little social
    support   c. men and women have less in common than same
    gender friends   d. both a and c   *e. all of the above

20. According to Watts (1970), if we try to control or possess
    this type of love, we are constantly doomed to disappointment.
    (p. 616)
    a. childhood love   b. friendship love   *c. erotic love
    d. humane love

21. This type of love includes emotional and physical intimacy
    (pp. 616-617)
    a. childhood love   b. erotic love   c. parental love
    *d. both a and b   e. all of the above

22. This type of love involves little or no expectation of any
    rewards other than the pleasure one obtains from caring for
    the other (p. 617)
    a. childhood love   b. erotic love   *c. parental love
    d. friendship love

23. This type of love involves one's devotion of time and energy
    to the welfare of others that one may not even know. (p. 617)
    a. being love   *b. humane love   c. parental love
    d. unconditional love

24. Which of the following characteristics is associated with
    falling in love? (p. 617)
    a. obsessional thoughts   b. clumsiness   c. shifting moods
    *d. all of the above

25. According to Berscheid and Walster (1974), defining our feel-
    ings as love is dependent on (p. 618)
    a. physiological arousal only   b. cognitive labeling only
    c. first labeling the emotion and then feeling the physio-
    logical arousal   *d. first feeling physiological arousal
    and then labeing it love

26. Berscheid and Walster (1974) believe that_____increases
    the likelihood of believing we are in love. (p. 618)
    a. anxiety   b. euphoria   c. sexual arousal
    *d. all of the above

27. Which of the following experiences are better explained by Berscheid and Walster's (1974) model than by Byrne's (1971) model? (p. 619)
a. unrequited love   b. jealousy   c. attraction and liking   *d. both a and b   e. all of the above

28. _____ has a theory of romantic love based on the concept of limerence. (p. 619)
a. Byrne   b. Berscheid and Walster   *c. Tennov   d. Rubin

29. Full blown limerence cannot develop without   (p. 619)
a. love   b. mutual trust   c. sexual intimacy   *d. uncertainty

30. Which of the following characterizes the limerent state? (p. 619)
a. reciprocity between the limerent and limerent object
b. sexual intimacy between the limerent and limerent object
*c. exclusivity with the limerent object   d. both a and b
e. all of the above

31. The first crystallization   in the development of limerence occurs after the object shows some sign of (p. 619)
*a. reciprocity   b. trust   c. love   d. uncertainty

32. Rubin's scale to measure love contains which of the following components? (p. 620)
a. trust   *b. exclusivity   c. sexual intimacy   d. both a and c   e. all of the above

33. Couples with higher love scores on Rubin's scale   (p. 620)
*a. spend more time gazing at each other   b. are more likely to be of the same religious faith   c. both a and b   d. neither a nor b

34. Concerning gender differences in loving and liking, Rubin found (p. 620)
a. women had higher love scores   b. men had higher love scores   *c. women liked their lovers more than men did   d. men liked their lovers more than women did   e. love scores and liking for one's lover were the same for both men and women

35. Lust is   (p. 621)
*a. normal   b. unhealthy   c. unpleasant   d. immoral

36. According to Dion and Dion (1973) which of the following personality types are more likely to report being in love? (p.622)
a. Type A personality   *b. external locus of control   c. high self-esteem   d. all of the above

196

37. The very first experience of love that most of us have is based on (p. 622)
    a. jealousy   *b. dependency   c. reciprocity   d. lust

38. The increasing need of two people to be with one another is labeled by Peele and Brodsky as (p. 622)
    a. infatuation   b. limerence   *c. tolerance   d. dependency

39. Peele and Brodsky (1976) use the analogy of_____to describe people's need for security through emotional attachment. (p. 622)
    a. obsessive hand-washing   b. agoraphobia (fear of open spaces)   c. students returning home after college
    *d. drug addiction

40. Liebowitz and Klein have suggested that "love sickness" may be in part caused by (p. 623)
    a. child abuse   b. low self-esteem   *c. a chemical similar to amphetamine   d. both a and b

41. The authors of the text believe that the concept of unconditional love applied to a relationship between adults often masks (p. 626)
    *a. dependency   b. jealousy   c. unhappiness   d. hostility

42. Concerning jealousy, White believes (p. 636)
    a. feelings of inadequacy cause jealousy in women
    b. reactions of jealousy lead to feelings of inadequacy in men   *c. both a and b   d. neither a nor b

43. White found that the most common motive for inducing jealousy in one's partner was to (p. 626)
    a. prove one's sexual attractiveness   b. show independence
    c. get back at one's partner   *d. attract attention

44. In response to jealousy (p. 627)
    a. women generally seek outside relationships for solace or retribution   b. men generally attempt to make themselves more sexually "macho"   c. both a and b
    *d. neither a nor b

45. Jealousy is more common (p. 627)
    a. among older people   b. among more educated people
    *c. in new relationships   d. all of the above

46. According to Miller, people spend much of their lives caught in the tension between (p. 627)
    a. sharing and privacy   *b. engulfment and abandonment
    c. trust and mistrust   d. self-love and selfishness

47. Which of the following is crucial for developing a loving relationship? (p. 629)
a. a sharing of all or most activities   *b. honesty, integrity, and concern for resolving problems
c. egalitarian roles in the relationship   d. sexual exclusivity   e. all of the above

48. Apfelbaum (1982) views loving sexual relationships as being invulnerable to   (p. 630)
a. jealousy   b. dependency   c. imperfection
*d. stress

TRUE-FALSE QUESTIONS

A single underscore indicates the correct answer.

T F 1. Harlow's studies with monkeys indicated that maladjustment caused by isolation from one's mother appears to be irreversible. (p. 610)

T F 2. Jealousy appears to be a universally experienced feeling in the context of sexual interaction of a mate with another person. (p. 626)

T F 3. The kind of care a monkey receives has a profound effect on its later behavior. (p. 609)

T F 4. Isolated female monkeys who have been impregnated accidentally or artificially are generally rejecting or incompetent mothers. (p. 610)

T F 5. Harlow and his colleagues found that a sort of monkey sex therapy procedure did little to change the behavior of isolated monkeys. (p. 610)

T F 6. Across cultures, Prescott found no relationship between the amount of physical affection used to raise infants and their subsequent display of physical violence. (p. 611)

T F 7. According to the authors of the text, when we love ourselves we are most capable of giving to and loving others. (p. 612)

T F 8. Current evidence supports Freud's contention that young children have a desire for sexual intercourse. (p. 616)

T F 9. Throughout most of our history, friendship between a man and a woman has been seen as unlikely or impossible. (p. 616)

T F 10. Humane love usually involves a give and take relationship. (p. 617)

<u>T</u> F 11. Many behaviors associated with emotional disturbance
           are also associated with falling in love.   (p. 617)

T <u>F</u> 12. Berscheid and Walster (1974) argue that loving is a
            stronger form of liking. (p. 618)

T <u>F</u> 13. Infatuation has long been a subject of intensive
            research. (p. 618)

T <u>F</u> 14. Berscheild and Walster (1974) explain love using
            Byrne's model of interpersonal attraction. (p. 618)

<u>T</u> F 15. Unlike love, limerence is an all or nothing state that
           is experienced in similar ways by men and women.
           (p. 619)

T <u>F</u> 16. Limerence appears to develop all at once rather than in
            stages. (p. 619)

<u>T</u> F 17. Nonlimerents are generally practical about their
           romantic involvements. (p. 620)

<u>T</u> F 18. Couples with higher love scores on Rubin's scale are
           more likely to eventually marry. (p. 620)

T <u>F</u> 19. According to the authors of the text, lust is a volun-
            tary response and not an involuntary feeling.
            (p. 620)

<u>T</u> F 20. Evidence suggests that young women are still more
           likely than young men to see love as necessary for sex.
           (p. 621)

<u>T</u> F 21. The authors of the text believe that if partners
           honestly communicate expectations, they can have healthy
           sexual relations based on lust. (p. 621)

<u>T</u> F 22. Romantic love is stereotypically perceived in our
           culture as a mysterious force that overwhelms the
           lover. (p. 622)

T <u>F</u> 23. According to Fromm, fatherly love, like motherly love,
            is unconditional. (p. 625)

T <u>F</u> 24. Even cultures with polygamous marriages are
            characterized by jealousy.   (p. 626)

T F 25. Women are more likely than men to report provoking jealousy in their partners. (p. 626)

T F 26. Bryson and Shettel-Neuber's (1978) research suggests that "revenge fucking" is more typical of men than it is of women. (p. 627)

T F 27. For most Americans, jealousy is a fact of life. (p. 627)

T F 28. The authors of the text believe it is important to set aside periods of leisure time for emotional and sexual interaction. (p. 627)

1 2 3 4 5 6 7 8 9 0